THE CHARLTON
STANDARD CATALOGUE OF

COALPORT FIGURINES

FIRST EDITION

By
Tom Power

Introduction
by
Gaye Blake Roberts

Jean Dale
Publisher

The Charlton Press

Toronto, Ontario • Birmingham, Michigan

CANADIAN CATALOGUING IN PUBLICATION DATA

The National Library of Canada has catalogued this publication as follows:

The Charlton standard catalogue of Coalport figurines

Biennial

1997-

ISSN 1482-8286

ISBN 0-88968-214-3 (1997 issue)

1. Coalport porcelain—2. Coalport China Company —Catalogs.
3. Figurines —England —Catalogs

NK4399.C55c43 738.8'2'029442 C97-901009-8

Printed in Canada
in the Province of Ontario

EDITORIAL

Publisher and Editor	Jean Dale
Assistant Editor	Nicola Leedham
Graphic Technician	Davina Rowan
Photography	Tom Power
Technical Consultant	Alf Willis

ACKNOWLEDGMENTS

The author and The Charlton Press wish to thank the following for their invaluable help:
Ray Atkins, Gaye Blake Roberts, Liz Bryant-Herron, Kate Cadman, The Coalport China Museum, Coalport Collectors Society, Collette Coleman, Compton and Woodhouse, Gary Darlow, Rinalda Demetriou, Richard Dennis Publications, Glenys Espley, Jade Ferguson, Mr. S. Harris, Ironbridge Gorge Museum Trust, Daphne Jones, Mike Lawton, Martha McKee, Ghyslaine and Renata Naufal, Liz Payne, Mrs. Isobel Pilkington, Joanne Riley, Alison Robb, Christine Smith, Mitch Tankosic, Eileen Walder, Peter Walklate, Waterford Wedgwood U.K., Waterford Wedgewood Canada Inc., David Weetman, Alf Willis, Sheila Wooliscroft.

The photograph of The Chinese Priest on page xii is by courtesy of The Trustees of The Wedgewood Museum, Barlaston, Stoke-on-Trent, Staffordshire, England.

A SPECIAL NOTE TO COLLECTORS

We would welcome and appreciate any comments or suggestion in regard to *The Charlton Standard Catalogue of Coalport Figurines* that you might have. If you would like to participate in pricing or supplying new data please call Jean Dale at (416) 488-1418 or contact Tom Power, 9 Church Street, London, England.

The Charlton Press

Editorial Office:
2040 Yonge Street, Suite 208
Toronto, Ontario M4S 1Z9
Tel: (416) 488-1418 Fax: (416) 488-4656
Tel: (800) 442-6042 Fax: (800) 442-1542

ALF WILLIS

Alf Willis was born in Burslem, Stoke-on-Trent in 1946. He was born into a family with a long tradition in the pottery industry. As well as his parents, pottery connections can be traced back four generations.

As a young boy, Alf would spend his free time at the Burslem School of Art where he remembers the distinctive smell of the oil paints and watching the artists at work. Throughout his school days his goal was to attend the Burslem School of Art. Unfortunately, this was impossible and the age of fifteen Alf entered the pottery profession to make his living.

During his career he has worked for some of the major pottery manufacturers of the world. Alf commenced work for Coalport, a subsidiary of the Wedgewood Group, at the beginning of the 1990s. When he joined the company, he was only one of twenty figure painters. Today the number of painters has increased approximately eight fold.

Although Alf is currently based at the Coalport Minerva factory, Fenton, a great portion of his working year consists of travelling both at home and abroad. He has made many appearances on both the television and radio including appearances in Australia and Canada.

Alf lives with his wife Lillian in Stoke-on-Trent and his two children. His two sisters and one brother have also followed careers with the ceramic industry, ensuring that the Willis family tradition is kept alive.

It is not surprising to hear that Alf is enjoying his work today as much as when he first began over thirty years ago. He admits that he still experiences a feeling of excitement as each figurine is transformed from a blank canvas into a work of art. Each individual piece is marked with the artist's monogram. His vast experience and skill are illustrated outwardly in his work which has provided him with the prestigious and honoured title of "Mastercraftsman" — a title which cannot be disputed.

TOM POWER

Tom Power was born in Glasgow in 1945. His family moved to London in 1950 where he was raised. For twenty years he owned a garage business restoring collectable and vintage cars. In 1980 he sold the business and in 1983 opened a small shop in a large central London Antiques market specialising in 20th Century discontinued ceramics.

In 1990 he moved nearby to his own shop, The Collector. The many requests for information on Coalport figures, both old and modern, over the years, together with the scant information available was the inspiration for this publication.

TABLE OF CONTENTS

Introduction vii
How to Use this Catalogue xiii
A Guide to Backstamps xiii
Coalport Figurines
1890 to 1976 1
1975 to the present 21
Collecting By Series 349

Boy Fishing, The Riding Lesson, Boy Boating, Bridesmaid (Style Three)
Pauline Shone's Children Studies

Coalport China Works

INTRODUCTION
By Gaye Blake Roberts

The concept of ceramic figures is as old as the art of pottery itself, the earliest examples being made for both pleasure and devotional religious acts. In England the tradition was probably stimulated by imported Oriental porcelain and the arrival during the 18th century of quantities of European porcelain figures. The popularity in Britain for figures corresponds with the birth of the consumer society, when many people had, for the first time, an amount of disposable income which could be spent on luxuries such as purely ornamental objects. The figures themselves demonstrate the change in fashion and taste. These fripperies were described in a contemporary Christie's catalogue of 1771 as being, "only for those who have superfluous money."

Pottery manufacture in the valley of the River Severn in Shropshire from the 17th century onwards was partially attributable to the deposits of alluvial clay and high quality coal, both of which contributed to the establishment of a number of small potteries providing wares to satisfy local demand. Throughout the 18th century earthenware was manufactured in a number of factories, including Benthall and Jackfield and a fine porcelain industry had been established with the founding of the Caughley Works, also known as The Royal Salopian Porcelain Manufactory, by Thomas Turner and Ambrose Gallimore, which was advertising its wares for sale by 1775.

Almost without exception the wares produced at Caughley were of a useful nature and there is no evidence of figure production in any quantity being executed.

In the history of Shropshire ceramics the story of the Coalport factory, which is the longest surviving, is probably the best known, producing a wide range of fine wares over a period of 130 years (until 1926) when the company moved to Staffordshire, the heart of the ceramic industry and ultimately in 1959 to its present location in Fenton, one of the celebrated "Five Towns."

John Rose was an experienced ceramic manufacturer when he opened the Coalport factory. He had been born nearby on February 8th, 1772, the son of a local farmer. Tradition suggests that he was apprenticed to Thomas Turner at Caughley where he learned all aspects of ceramic production. It seems probable that he left Turner's employment during the early 1790s and that he joined forces with Edward Blakeway about 1793, the year of his majority, starting a ceramic factory at Jackfield. A reference to this short-lived venture occurs in a Wedgwood and Byerley ledger of accounts for the 31st December 1794, where there is an entry made out to "John Rose Esq . of Calcut China Manufactory." Not much information is known about Edward Blakeway, but he appears to be have been a wealthy business man and influential member of the local society, including being Mayor of Shrewsbury (the county town) in 1755, prior to him moving to Broseley Hall where he pursued an interest in the local iron trade. There is nothing in the early history of Blakeway to suggest an interest in the ceramic industry but it may have been that the older man was prepared to back the ambitions and recognized the ability of the young twenty-one-year old John Rose.

The ceramic tradition within the area was an important factor in the creation of the Coalport factory, which was established on the northern banks of the River Severn about 1795 in an area which can best be described as a "New Town," and was the creation of the industrialist and entrepreneur William Reynolds. The area was the cradle of the Industrial Revolution and with the completion in 1790 of the eastern branch of the Shropshire Canal which linked into the River Severn at Coalport, the adjacent land became an ideal location for new development. In September 1793 William Reynolds leased from his father Richard, the meadows with the idea of building, "Houses Warehouse ... Wharfs, Quays, Landing places, Crane Weigh Beams or other erections" The first reference to this development being called Coalport occurs in the records of the local Horsehay Company on 13th May, 1794. It seems probable that Rose and Blakeway moved to this new site sometime before the end of 1795 as there is a reference to clay and fire bricks being supplied to "John Rose (China Manufactory) at Coalport" in December of that year, whilst further supplies from the Horsehay Company arrived at regular intervals throughout 1796 and 1797. The materials would almost certainly have been used in the construction of the factory rather than in the production of porcelain. The works consisted of a long narrow building, parallel to the road and built on the stretch of land between the canal and the highway.

It is probable that Richard Rose (born September 20th, 1774), John's younger brother, joined the firm at its inception at Coalport as a junior partner. At the same time the company name seems to have been formalized from "Blakeway & Rose China Manufactory" to the better known, "John Rose & Co.." It is also possible that the change coincided with the commercial production of their ceramics which had evidently reached a degree of perfection enough to entice the nobility, as described in the local paper the Shropshire Journal of August 24th , 1796 when it reported: "Their Highnesses the Prince and Princess of Orange .... visited the Dale Company's Ironworks ...went by water to see Mr. Brodie's Canon Foundary ... and thence proceeded to the china factory at Coal-park where his Highness bought some pieces of Mr. Rose: and viewing the Tar Spring the inclined Plane etc. returned to the Tontine Inn." The place name "Coal-park" is almost certainly the area known as Coalport especially as the newspapers of that period contained many such minor typographical errors.

An excellent description of the area was given by Thomas Telford in November 1800 which appeared in Joseph Plymley's "General View of the Agriculture of Shropshire" published in 1803. It reads: "Formerly the place (Coalport) consisted of a very rugged uncultivated bank, which scarcely produced even grass, but owing to the judicious regulations and encouragement of Mr. Reynolds, joined to the benefits arising from the canal and the river, houses to the number of 30 have been built there and more are still wanted, to accommodate the people employed at a large china manufactory ..." By 1797 the Coalport partners entered into an agreement to take over further property at Coalport effectively trebling their land holding by this transaction. Further evidence of their success and expansion occurs in various documents relating to the acquisition of large quantities of clay during the early months of 1798. One year later, in October 1799, the Coalport Works had expanded to such an extent that the following advertisement was inserted in the Shropshire Journal on October2nd and 9th:

"COALPORT CHINA MANUFACTORY

Workmen wanted in the gilding, enamelling and blue-painting lines: 12 good hands of each will meet with constant employ." Curiously this advertisement appeared just two days before an agreement signed between Thomas Turner of Caughley and John Rose of Coalport in which Turner retired from porcelain production and relinquished his manufacturing works to the younger man. From then until 1814 when the lease ran out on the Caughley factory, Rose ran both sites concurrently producing a wide range of both useful and ornamental wares. Unfortunately, tragedy struck some of the Coalport employees within the month. The events were described by John Rose himself when he wrote to the Editor of the Shropshire Journal giving a first-hand account. Written from Coalport on October 26th, 1799, he describes the events: "As there will be many erroneous accounts circulating respecting the unfortunate and shocking accident that happened here on Wednesday evening (October 23rd) at 9 o'clock, I beg leave to state as near particulars as I have yet been able to learn. As the people from the Coalport manufactory, to the number of 43 were leaving there at 9 o'clock at night, to go home over the usual passage boat, owing to the in-attention of the man whom the boatman had entrusted to steer over, the boat unfortunately went down with all on board, when only 15 out of the whole could save themselves, the remaining 28 were unfortunately lost. In consequence of the great fog and the darkness of the night, no one was able to give the least assistance."

There follows a list of the persons drowned - comprising 6 men, 5 boys and fourteen women and children together with three workers who it would appear worked at Walter Bradley's Pottery manufactory on an adjacent site at Coalport. Undoubtedly, many of the workers had been drawn from the old established potting centres on the other side of the river. Less than a year later the numbers engaged in the manufacture of china was reputed to be 250. The extensive factory had been described by C. Hackett in his diary of "A Tour through the Counties of England and Wales" written in 1796 as: "the largest, and probably the most expensive, porcelain producing estate in Great Britain."

The history of porcelain production at Coalport, however, is not a simple story because in June 1800 a new company was founded making a similar style of porcelain in premises opposite to the established works of John Rose but located between the river and the canal. Literally the two factories were separated by the width of the narrow Shropshire Canal. The second works was under the auspices of William Reynolds, William Horton, Thomas Rose (the second brother of John) and after 1803, Robert Antice following the death of William Reynolds. As far as can be ascertained this second Coalport factory did not manufacture any figures and therefore can be largely ignored in the story of figure production at Coalport. It is important however to note that John Rose & Co. acquired this second factory when it was advertised for sale in 1814. It was an astute business move especially as the Caughley site lease was about to expire and it was far more practical and convenient to have an enlarged manufacturing area so close together. It is possible that the extended and improved site made the company's remarkable achievements in the 19th century possible.

In the intervening years, John Rose had suffered from the political and more especially the economic uncertainties which affected most of the industry. During this period Rose seems to have had a series of financial backers but it did not prevent the company's bankruptcy in 1803 which can in part at least be attributed to their banking activities rather than a failure of their ceramic business. They are described in the bankruptcy papers as "Porcelain Manufacturers and Bankers." The factory was advertised for sale in the local papers on September 21st and 28th, 1803 when it was acquired by Cuthbert Johnson and William Clarke who appear to have had the capital but no ceramic experience ultimately retaining Rose as their manager. The advertisement provides a good indication as to the size and importance of the factory including in the Bill of Sale, "Warehouses, Counting houses, Kilns, stove houses and all other buildings necessary for carrying on the porcelain manufactory to a very great extent. Also all the machinery, implements, utensils and tools thereto belonging together with a large stock of china, materials, ingredients and other articles necessary for carrying on the said works and also 12 Dwelling Houses adjoining thereto." The advertisement further details the lease which was originally for 21 years of which 14 were unexpired at an annual rent of £61. 14s. 2d. Effectively the consumer would have probably not noticed a change in ownership at Coalport as the new partnership left John Rose to dominate and organize the day to day production.

Tradition suggests that Rose expanded again during 1820 acquiring the assistance of skilled craftsmen from the factories at Nantgarw and Swansea in South Wales. At the same time several improvements were made to the Coalport body and glaze which had previously been predominantly lead-based and consequently damaging to the workers health through the notorious "Potter's Rot." For his introduction of a leadless felspathic glaze Rose was awarded "The Isis Gold Medal" from the Society of Arts (later to become the Royal Society of Arts) on May 30th, 1820. Immediately this was incorporated into the Coalport backstamp. The products of this period were generally categorized by the translucency of body and fine decoration aided by the addition to the decorating department of five skilled artists formerly employed at the Derby manufactory. At this period Rose also introduced the distinctive range of Rococo style of flower-encrusted ornamental pieces now generally referred to as "Coalbrookdale" wares, (Coalbrookdale being the name generally given to the whole region). It was with this group of wares that Rose could be said to have manufactured figures for the first time.

A very few were manufactured individually, whilst others were designed to be applied to such pieces as candlesticks and vases, though the company is better known for the addition of naturalistic moulded flowers which appear in great profusion. This range of ware is well illustrated in a curious manuscript described as a Traveller's Note Book, formerly the property of William Hedley who describes himself on the flyleaf as a " Willm Hedley, Traveller for Mess. John Rose & Co. Coalport, near Ironbridge," and who lived in the nearby town of Madeley, near Wellington, Shropshire. The notebook is a compilation of beautifully executed water-colour drawings of the pieces available and their prices together with others which are uncoloured printed outlines, many of which date from the late 1820s through to the middle years of the century. The book includes one illustration of an important figure group made in the new Parian body which must post-date 1847.

John Rose died on October 30th, 1841, aged 69 years, leaving behind a company that was financially secure and considered to be amongst the best manufacturers in the country, enjoying Royal Patronage of the young Queen Victoria and many other influential patrons. On John Rose's death his interest in the works seems to have passed jointly back to his brother Thomas Rose and to John Rose's nephew, William Frederick Rose (born April 3rd, 1809). Thomas Rose was to have only a brief interest in the firm as he died less than two years later. The other two partners at this time are listed as Charles Maddison and another local Salopian, William Pugh. Together W.F. Rose and Pugh guided the company through the next few years when the proprietors must have hoped for a period of consolidation and stability following the enforced changes which occurred in the two years between 1841 and 1843.

The Coalport company prospered and in 1845 through the London retailers, Messrs. A.B. & R.P. Daniells, of 129 New Bond Street & Wigmore Street they received a commission from the Queen to prepare a dessert service which was to be presented to the Emperor of Russia, Czar Nicholas I on the occasion of his visit to England. The company also produced a range of special commissions for John and Thomas Staples who were responsible for supplying the victuals and table china for many of the major events in the city of London including the opening of the Royal Exchange in 1844, the Coal Exchange in 1849, and a magnificent service which was prepared for a dinner to mark the opening of the Great Exhibition of 1851 and later for Royal visits of the Emperor Napoleon III and Empress Eugenie of France in April, 1855 and the King and Queen of Sardinia later in the same year.

At the Great Exhibition of 1851 Coalport not only exhibited in their own right under the name of "John Rose & Co., Coalbrook Dale, Ironbridge, Shropshire" but contributed significantly to Daniells' stand, who could be described as Coalport's largest retailer. Amongst the range of prestigious pieces Coalport exhibited a number of figurative groups in the newly developed Parian body. The origins of the Parian body can be traced to the biscuit porcelain figures of a century earlier which were associated with the manufactories of Sèvres in France and the Derby factory owned by William Duesbury in England. By the time the Derby figures were in decline a number of other English Potteries had entered into the production of white ceramic figures most of whom were using a bone china body including Minton, Worcester, Copeland & Garrett, Rockingham and Coalport.

The early history of Parian is difficult to define as it was a natural development from the unglazed bone china which was in use by many potters and which was not wholly satisfactory due to the porosity of the body which was subject to staining and difficult to clean. The first claimant for the perfection, during the 1840s, of a "New Body" which subsequently became known as Parian was Thomas Battam, the manager of the Art Department at the Copeland Works, and subsequently one of the founders of the Crystal Palace Art Union. This new material, which closely resembled marble, was called "Statuary Porcelain" by Battam. Other factories were working contemporaneously to produce a similar material and the most probable date for the general introduction of this new body was during 1845.

Once the Parian pieces became available, they proved to be extremely successful and popular after being exhibited regularly at the various exhibitions nationwide from 1846 onwards. However, by the Great Exhibition of 1851, ten of the leading manufacturers, including Coalport, showed Parian amongst their displays to considerable critical acclaim. Parian was, from its introduction, sold on its artistic merits and aimed to satisfy the increased demand created by the middle classes.

Coalport seems to have been surprising early in the field of Parian production with at least one piece datable to 1847. A portrait bust survives inscribed, "Jany. 1847 by Permission of Thos. Smith," who appears to have been a wealthy saddler of the nearby town of Shifnal, Shropshire. One of the most striking Coalport Parian groups is that variously described as, "Beauty and the Beast" or the "Cat and Monkey," which shows a young lady, fashionably attired wearing a cat-mask, with a monkey figure in male costume. It is possible that the theme is an adaptation of John Gay's fables, first published in 1727 and subsequently illustrated in 1779 by Thomas Bewick and again by Charles Muss (who also engraved a view of the Coalport Works), published in 1825. Fable Fourteen was entitled, "The Monkey who has seen the World" and could possibly be the inspiration for this group which is illustrated in the William Hedley Traveller's Note Book where it is annotated as being 8 inches high and cost 18/- (eighteen shillings).

Cat and Monkey

Two Coalport Parian portraits of the Duke of Wellington are recorded. The first is a bust made in 1853 after a study produced by Henry Weigall from life whilst the second portrait of the Duke sitting with his legs outstretched and his arms crossed is based on a statuette by George Abbott. It is probable that both studies were manufactured in memory of the Duke who died in September 1852 and who was generally regarded as a national hero. Other portrait busts included two studies of Lord Nelson (1758-1805) one of which is described as "Modelled under the direction of Admiral Sir William Parker KCB from a painting by Wichell in his collection," both versions, however were modelled by Joseph Pitts and were available by 1853. Another bust modelled by Pitts made at Coalport was that of Sir Robert Peel, (born 1778) the Prime Minister, which was made to commemorate his death in July, 1850. Three less well-known Coalport Parian busts include models of George Stephenson (1781-1848), the inventor and founder of the railway after constructing the first locomotive in 1814, modelled by E.W. Wyon about 1858; a bust of R.D. Gray attributed to the modelling of E. Bacon was manufactured about 1855 and the head of Harriet Martineau (1802-1876) an author, especially of children's stories, whose statue is inscribed, "Thos Smith Fecit, published by Deville & Co. 367 Strand, London. January 18th, 1849." The announcement of the engagement of Edward Prince of Wales to Princess Alexander in 1863 gave Coalport the opportunity to produce a pair of likenesses which are inscribed, "John Rose & Co. Coalport. Feby. 18. 1863. Made to commemorate the Prince of Wales engagement."

Princess Alexandra and Edward, Prince of Wales

As was common with many manufactories the most spectacular and elaborate Coalport figure groups such as "The Pleiades adorning Light " were produced for display at the International Exhibitions are listed in the companies official entry for the 1851 Great Exhibition. Other Parian groups exhibited at the Crystal Palace included a "Pair of Wrestling figures" and "Puck and his companions," which is probably the best known of this group as it was reproduced in the contemporary Art-Journal Catalogue. The compiler of the catalogue, noted, "it is a clever design and the figures are admirably modelled: it is, we believe, the work of the late admirable sculptor, Mr. Pitts as finished by his son." The company must have been proud of the figure as it was re-exhibited at the Dublin exhibition of 1853.

"The Pleiades adorning Light"

It is probable that these groups were never manufactured on a commercial scale, more in the nature of "one-offs" especially for exhibition purposes. On their stand apart from the figures mentioned the Coalport company included a number of centrepieces where the pierced baskets were supported for example by, "Cupids in Parian, representing the Seasons," or a "smaller épergne, supported by sea-horses in Parian," and a "Basket, supported by three female figures, Parian."

It seems evident that the Coalport company made a considerable effort to extend its range of Parian models for the Dublin exhibition and only a year later in 1854, they were announcing that they were issuing a number of Parian statues "several subjects modelled by Pitts from *The Faery Queen*. The account makes specific reference to four subjects which were modelled by Joseph Pitts a talented sculptor who exhibited at the Royal Academy between 1842 and 1870. He modelled romantic scenes from Edmund Spencer's (1552 -1599) classical epic poem "The Faerie Queene" including; "Sir Calepine rescuing Serena," "Britomartis unveiling Amoret," "Britomartis releasing Amoret" and "The Vision of the Red Crosse Knight." These subjects would have been particularly popular with the Victorians as they would have conformed to their love of the heroic and historical literary connotations.

The retirement of W.F. Rose in 1862, leaving William Pugh as the sole proprietor, seemed to have marked a significant change in the fortunes of the Coalport company. On June 19th, 1875 Pugh died owing a considerable amount of money to his bank and other creditors who had supplied him with raw materials, resulting in the bank requesting his executors to carry on the business with a view to it ultimately being closed. By the Autumn of 1876 an official Receiver had been appointed. In 1888 the Coalport company comprising, "The

"Sir Calepine Rescuing Serena"

Works and premises at Coalport, Manchester and London, with the Leases Stock in trade, Materials Book debts Machinery Implements and all other articles and effects," were purchased to the sum of £15,000 by an East Anglian engineer, Peter Schulyer Bruff. He seems to have had no previous connections with the ceramic industry and his reasons for the purchase have never really been clear. Peter Bruff's son, Charles, became the Managing Director in 1888 with Thomas Bott as his Manager. Together they instigated a policy of efficiency and new standards in an attempt to restore the factory to its previous position within the ceramic industry and to something of its former glory.

It was during the 1880s that a limited number of white figures were produced including a "man carrying a two handled basket" which would appear to have been made with a female companion. It is interesting to note that at the time of Peter Bruff's death amongst his effects are listed, "a pair of white Coalport figures - a man and a woman." Similarly there is also recorded a large sized model of a monkey, based on the Meissen model by J.J. Kaëndler .

It would appear that the introduction of these figures coincided with the employment of E. Bertram Mackennal, an Australian sculptor, who obtained from about 1886, "a position as head of the art department at a pottery at Coalport." It is evident from some of the factory records that white porcelain continued to be popular through to the early years of the 20th century.

In 1889 Peter Bruff changed the status of the firm into a private company with limited liability, taking the opportunity to change the name at the same time to the Coalport China Company (John Rose & Co.) Ltd. The increased creativity instigated by Bott from about 1889-90, was remarkable and could be seen especially in the range of ornamental wares he introduced. Amongst this group are some of the earliest Coalport figurines, as we know them today, such as the figure of a Jester and a Costermonger. About 1914, there were also some experimental figures manufactured including a model of a Polar Bear covered with a "pearlised" surface which was an uncertain attempt to improve the company's deteriorating financial position. The

The Jester

1920s saw a revival of this figurine tradition with a variety of figures such as the Balloon Ladies, the first of the true Crinoline Ladies, and a model of a Medieval lady, and a French aristocrat possibly depicting Monsieur Beaucaire. A charming group of six individual figures referred to as "The Wedding Group," were the creation of Percy Simpson who worked at Coalport, principally as a painter, from 1901 to 1926 before continuing his work for the company after their move to Stoke-on-Trent. Many of these early figures continued in production after the closure of the factory in Shropshire.

The geographical isolation, a depressed home market and industrial action by the workers inevitably led to the sale of the Coalport China Company in 1925 to the Cauldon Potteries Limited. However, the actual closure of the Coalport Works with the transfer of the moulds, equipment and many of the workers to Shelton, Staffordshire, eventually occurred after a winding down period in April, 1926. Cauldon, an old established company only owned the Coalport concern for ten years before they were both acquired by the Crescent Pottery under George Jones & Sons Limited and were moved again to Stoke. During this period Coalport maintained its individuality with the continuation in production of numerous figurines. Some most unusual items created during this period included a range called "Jade" comprising at least four earthenware figures in the Oriental manner including a "Chinese Priest," "Buddha," "Chinese Boat" and "Chinese Dog," all painted according to the "V" pattern book, by Percy Simpson about 1938.

The Chinese Priest

At the outbreak of the Second World War figure production dropped to almost nil as more essential War work and utility items were manufactured. By 1949 the figures were reintroduced with a range of traditional type ladies released first, including Jennifer, Rosalinda, tiny crinoline figures called Kitty and Joan, as well as an exotic Spanish dancer and a clown. Coalport survived another change of ownership in 1958 when it was taken over by E. Brain & Co., an old family china business under their Chairman, Mr. E.W. Brain. In a radio interview he stated that it was his intention to continue Coalport, "with all its charm of once-upon-a time." From the late 1960s, plans were laid to extend the range further both with new models and the reintroduction of some of the earlier figures. In 1973 a team of talented young modellers were employed to inject new life into the traditional range and it is from this time that Coalport figurine production can truly be said to have blossomed.

Gaye Blake Roberts

OTHER INFORMATION

HOW TO USE THIS CATALOGUE

The Listings

This book has been designed to serve two specific purposes. First, to furnish the Coalport enthusiast with accurate listings containing vital information and photographs to aid in the building of a rewarding collection. Secondly, this publication provides Coalport collectors and dealers with current market prices for the complete line of Coalport figurines.

Within the individual listings, the pieces are listed in alphabetical order. After the item's name comes Designer, the date of Issue and withdrawal, Size, Colour(s), and Variations. The Series to which the piece belongs (if applicable) is listed next. Lastly, the suggested retail price is given in American, Canadian and British funds.

A Note On Pricing

In addition to providing accurate information, this catalogue gives readers the most up-to-date retail prices for Coalport Figurines in American, Canadian and British currencies.

To accomplish this, The Charlton Press continues to access an international pricing panel of Coalport experts that submits prices based on both dealer and collector retail price activity. These market prices are carefully analysed and adjusted to reflect accurate valuations in each of these three markets.

Please be aware that all prices given in a particular currency are for figures within that particular country. The prices published herein have not been calculated using exchange rates exclusively. They have been determined solely by supply and demand within the country in question.

A necessary word of caution. No pricing catalogue can be, or should be, a fixed price list. This catalogue, therefore, should be considered as a pricing guide only - showing the most current retail prices based on market demand within a particular region for the various items.

Current figurines, however, are priced differently in this catalogue. Such pieces are priced according to the manufacturer's suggested retail price in each of the three market regions. It should be noted it is likely dealer discounting from these prices will occur.

Prices published herein are for pieces in mint condition. Collectors are cautioned that a repaired or restored piece may be worth as little as 50 per cent of the value of the same piece in mint condition. The collector interested strictly in investment potential will avoid damaged figurines.

Insuring Your Figurines

As with any other of your valuables, making certain your figurines are protected is a very important concern. It is paramount that you display or store any porcelain items is a secure place — preferably one safely away from traffic in the home.

Your figurines are most often covered under your basic homeowner's policy and there are generally three kinds of such policies —standard, broad and comprehensive. Each has its own specific deductible and terms.

Under a general policy, your figurines are considered "contents" and are covered for all of the perils covered under the contractual terms of your policy (fire, theft, water damage and so on).

However, since figurines are extremely delicate, breakage is treated differently by most insurance companies. There is usually an extra premium attached to insure figurines against accidental breakage by or carelessness of the owner. This is sometimes referred to as a "fine arts" rider.

You are advised to contact your insurance professional to get all the answers.

In order to help you protect yourself, it is critical that you take inventory of your figurines and have colour photographs taken of all your pieces. This is the surest method of clearly establishing, for the police and your insurance company, the items lost or destroyed. It is also the easiest way to establish their replacement value in the event of a tragedy.

A Guide to Backstamps

This is the first attempt to chronologically list the Coalport backstamps so that they may aid the reader to date their figurines. Please do remember that it is the first attempt and will most certainly need to be revised as more and more backstamp data is accumulated.

BLACK BACKSTAMP: 1900 to 1930s

Figurine name in script
Coalport factory mark

GREEN BACKSTAMP: 1940s to 1970s

Figurine name in script
Coalport factory mark

ORANGE BACKSTAMP: 1973 - 1974

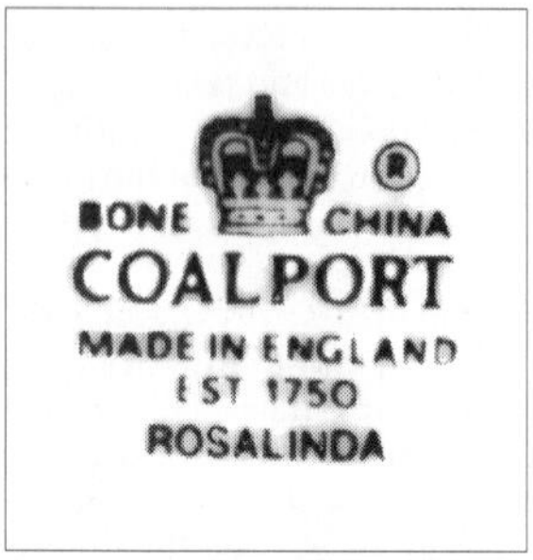

Figurine name in block capital letters
Coalport factory mark with bone china added
Possibly only used on reblocked figurines

BLUE BACKSTAMP: 1974 - 1992

First blue backstamp 1974 - 1981

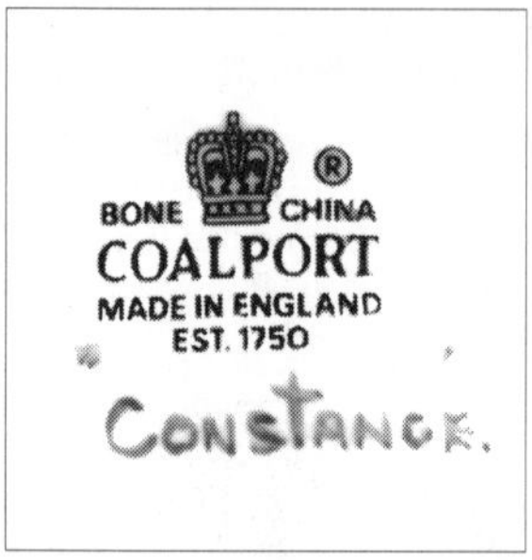

Figurine name hand written in block upper and lower case letters
Coalport factory mark with bone china

Figurine name in block upper and lower case letters
Coalport factory mark with bone china

Second blue backstamp c.1981

Figurine name in block letters
Coalport factory mark without bone china

Third blue backstamp 1982 - c.1985

Figurine name in script
Coalport factory mark with bone china
"Hand-painted by" added

Fourth blue backstamp c.1985 - c.1992

Figurine name in script
Coalport factory mark with fine bone china
Modeller's name, decorator's initials
Assembler's mark. Date of manufacture
© Coalport copyright date

GREY BACKSTAMP: 1992 to date

First grey backstamp c.1992 - 1994

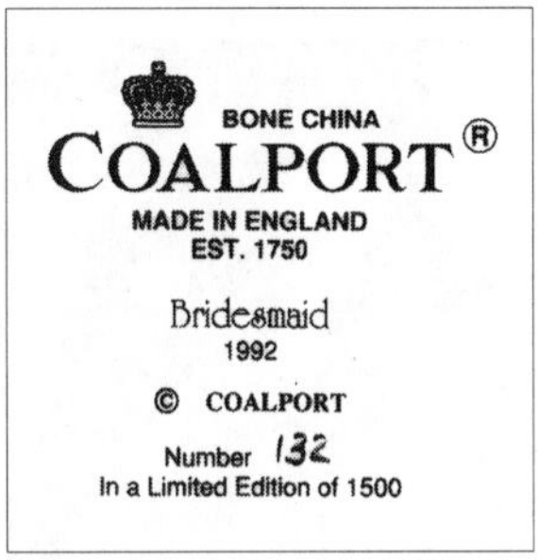

Backstamp in various typestyles
Name in upper and lower case
Coalport factory mark with bone china

Second grey backstamp —1994 - 1997

Backstamp in various type styles
Modified Coalport factory mark with bone china
Name in upper and lower case srcipt italics
The modeller's name, the marks of the assembler, caster, gilder, lithographer and painter, the mould identification number and the date of manufacture

Third grey backstamp — 1994 - 1997

Backstamp in various type styles
Modified Coalport factory mark with porcelain added
Name in upper and lower case italics
The marks of the assembler, caster, lithographer and painter, the mould identification number and the date of manufacture

The following is the backstamp
of Anne of Green Gables (Style One)
Issued 1982 - blue backstamp

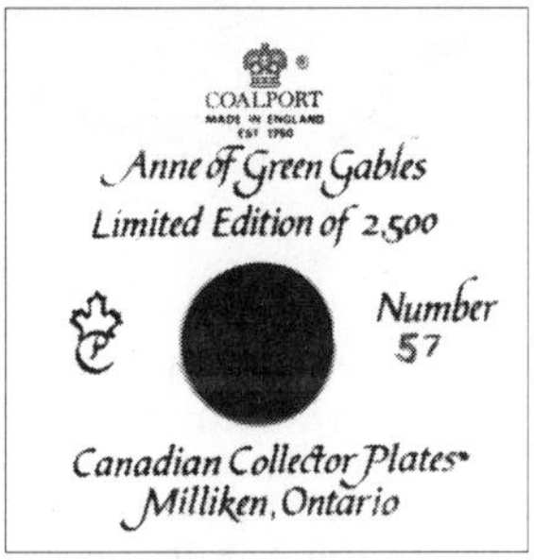

UNTITLED GIRL

Can you help with the above illustration?

Regardless of how much information you gather, there is always something that is unobtainable. The figurine illustrated above is indicative of such an occurence. While we have the photograph, we have been unsuccessful in finding out anything else about her. We would be most appreciative if you know anything about our "Untitled Girl," or can supply any data or photographs we are missing, if you could contact us at our editorial office: The Charlton Press, 2040 Yonge Street, Suite 208, Toronto, Ontario, M4S 1Z9, Canada. Those collectors providing information which is used in the second edition of *The Charlton Standard Catalogue of Coalport Figurines* will receive acknowledgement in the contributor's section.

COALPORT FIGURINES
1890 - 1976

Miniature Crinoline Ladies

Annette
Style One

Designer: Unknown
Height: 6 ¼", 15.9 cm
Colour: 1. Pink and mauve dress; pink shawl and bonnet
2. Green dress; pink shawl and bonnet
Issued: c.1920

Colourways	Backstamp	U.S. $	Can. $	U.K. £
1. Green	Black	525.00	600.00	350.00
2. Pink and mauve	Green	525.00	600.00	350.00

Annette
Style Two

Designer: Unknown
Height: 5 ¾", 14.6 cm
Colour: Yellow dress with pink collar; beige hat with flowers and lilac-pink ribbons
Issued: c.1949 - 1972

Name	Backstamp	U.S. $	Can. $	U.K. £
Annette (Style Two)	Green	475.00	550.00	325.00

Audrey

Designer: Unknown
Height: 3 ¾", 9.5 cm
Colour: Pink dress; yellow shawl; green hat
Issued: 1. c.1949 - 1972
2. 1973 - 1976
Series: Miniature Crinoline Ladies

Name	Backstamp	U.S. $	Can. $	U.K. £
Audrey	Blue	375.00	425.00	250.00

Note: This is a reblocked figurine. It probably exists with either a black or green backstamp.

Balloon Seller (Man)

Designer: Unknown
Height: 5 ½", 14.0 cm
Colour: Brown jacket; tan trousers and hat; yellow waistcoat; coloured balloons
Issued: c.1920

Name	Backstamp	U.S. $	Can. $	U.K. £
Balloon Seller (Man)	Black	550.00	650.00	375.00

Photograph not available at press time

Balloon Seller (Woman)

Designer: Unknown
Height: 5 ¼", 13.3 cm
Colour: Purple dress, green shawl, white apron; coloured balloons
Issued: c.1920

Name	Backstamp	U.S. $	Can. $	U.K. £
Balloon Seller (Woman)	Black	550.00	650.00	375.00

Barbara

Designer:	Unknown
Height:	5", 12.7 cm
Colour:	1. Lilac dress 2. Pink dress, blue shawl; mauve and yellow fan; green chair 3. Turquoise dress
Issued:	1. c.1949 - 1972 2. 1973 - 1976
Series:	Ladies of Fashion

Colourways	Backstamp	U.S. $	Can. $	U.K. £
1. Lilac	Orange	400.00	475.00	275.00
2. Pink	Orange	400.00	475.00	275.00
3. Turquoise	Orange	400.00	475.00	275.00

Note: This is a reblocked figurine. It probably exists with either a black or green backstamp.

Best Man

Designer:	Percy Simpson
Height:	5", 12.7 cm
Colour:	Black coat and shoes; blue waistcoat and tie; tan trousers; white shirt and socks; red hair
Issued:	c.1920
Series:	The Bridal Party

Name	Backstamp	U.S. $	Can. $	U.K. £
Best Man	Black	375.00	425.00	250.00

Breeze
Style One

Designer:	John Bromley
Height:	6 ¼", 15.5 cm
Colour:	1. Blue dress with white undershirt; blue bonnet, green ribbon 2. Orange-brown dress; tan bonnet with blue ribbon 3. Pink dress
Issued:	1. c.1949 - 1972 2. 1973 - 1976
Series:	Ladies of Fashion

Colourways	Backstamp	U.S. $	Can. $	U.K. £
1A. Blue dress	Green	250.00	300.00	175.00
1B. Blue dress	Orange	250.00	300.00	175.00
2. Orange-brown dress	Orange	250.00	300.00	175.00
3. Pink dress	Orange	250.00	300.00	175.00

Note: This is a reblocked figure.

Bride
(Style One)

Designer: Percy Simpson
Height: 5″, 12.7 cm
Colour: White dress and veil; bouquet of yellow flowers
Issued: c.1920
Series: The Bridal Party

Name	Backstamp	U.S. $	Can. $	U.K. £
Bride (Style One)	Black	375.00	425.00	250.00

Bridegroom

Designer: Percy Simpson
Height: 5″, 12.7 cm
Colour: Black coat and shoes; blue waistcoat and tie; tan trousers; white shirt and socks; brown hair
Issued: c.1920
Series: The Bridal Party

Name	Backstamp	U.S. $	Can. $	U.K. £
Bridegroom	Black	375.00	425.00	250.00

Bridesmaid
Style One

Designer: Percy Simpson
Height: 5″, 12.7 cm
Colour: Blue dress and hat; yellow and red bouquet of flowers
Issued: c.1920
Series: The Bridal Party

Name	Backstamp	U.S. $	Can. $	U.K. £
Bridesmaid (Style One)	Black	375.00	425.00	250.00

Bridesmaid
Style Two

Designer: Unknown
Height: 5 ½", 14.0 cm
Colour: Blue and mauve dress; lilac bonnet with purple ribbon
Issued: c.1949 - 1972

Name	Backstamp	U.S. $	Can. $	U.K. £
Bridesmaid (Style Two)	Black	375.00	425.00	250.00

Clarrisa
Style One

Designer: Unknown
Height: 7 ¼", 18.4 cm
Colour: Lilac and white dress; beige bonnet with red ribbon
Issued: c.1949 - 1972

Name	Backstamp	U.S. $	Can. $	U.K. £
Clarrisa (Style One)	Green	375.00	425.00	250.00

Clown

Designer: Unknown
Height: 9 3/4", 24.7 cm
Colour: Cream coat with black dots and turquoise trim; cream hat
Issued: 1. c.1949 - 1972
2. 1974 - 1976

Name	Backstamp	U.S. $	Can. $	U.K. £
Clown	Green	550.00	650.00	375.00

Note: This is a reblocked figurine. It probably exists with either an orange or blue backstamp.

Costermonger

Designer: Unknown
Height: Unknown
Colour: Red shirt; brown jacket; light brown trousers; blue hat and scarf
Issued: c.1914

Name	Backstamp	U.S. $	Can. $	U.K. £
Costermonger	Black		Rare	

Daisy
Style One

Designer: Unknown
Height: 4 ½", 11.9 cm
Colour: 1. Blue bodice, pale blue and purple skirt
2. Yellow dress with pink highlights
Issued: c.1920 - 1972

Colourways	Backstamp	U.S. $	Can. $	U.K. £
1. Blue dress	Green	400.00	475.00	275.00
2. Yellow dress	Black	400.00	475.00	275.00

Doris

Designer: Unknown
Height: 4 ½", 11.9 cm
Colour: Pink skirt, purple bodice with blue frills; blue underskirt; purple bonnet with blue ribbon
Issued: c.1949 - 1972

Name	Backstamp	U.S. $	Can. $	U.K. £
Doris	Green	480.00	560.00	320.00

Edyth

Designer: Unknown
Height: 5 ¾", 14.6 cm
Colour: 1. Green dress with purple frills; black bonnet with yellow ribbon
2. Pink dress with blue frills; pink bonnet with blue ribbon and bow
Issued: c.1920 - 1972

Name	Backstamp	U.S. $	Can. $	U.K. £
1. Green dress	Black	550.00	650.00	375.00
2. Pink dress	Green	550.00	650.00	375.00

Gwenda

Designer: Unknown
Height: 5 ¼", 13.0 cm
Colour: Rose-pink dress with blue frills
Issued: c.1920

Name	Backstamp	U.S. $	Can. $	U.K. £
Gwenda	Black	625.00	750.00	425.00

Her Ladyship

Designer: Unknown
Height: 4 ¾", 12.1 cm
Colour: Red dress; purple shawl; brown chair
Issued: c.1949 - 1972

Name	Backstamp	U.S. $	Can. $	U.K. £
Her Ladyship	Green	625.00	750.00	425.00

Isobel

Designer: Unknown
Height: 7", 17.8 cm
Colour: Mottled purple dress with green neckline; green bonnet with red flowers
Issued: c.1949 - 1972

Name	Backstamp	U.S. $	Can. $	U.K. £
Isobel	Green	475.00	550.00	325.00

Jennifer Jane

Designer: Unknown
Height: 6", 15.0 cm
Colour: 1. Purple
2. Turquoise dress with pink edging; pink bonnet with turquoise ribbon; basket of apples
Issued: 1. c.1949 - 1972
2. 1973 - 1976
Series: Ladies of Fashion

Colourways	Backstamp	U.S. $	Can. $	U.K. £
1. Purple dress	Orange	240.00	280.00	160.00
2. Turquoise dress	Orange	240.00	280.00	160.00

Note: This is a reblocked figurine. It probably exists with either a black or green backstamp.

Jessica
Style One

Designer: Unknown
Height: 3 ½", 8.9 cm
Colour: Blue dress; rose-pink bonnet; basket of flowers
Issued: 1. c.1949 - 1972
2. 1973 - 1976
Series: Miniature Crinoline Lady

Name	Backstamp	U.S. $	Can. $	U.K. £
Jessica (Style One)	Blue	400.00	475.00	275.00

Note: This is a reblocked figurine. It probably exists with either a black or green backstamp.

Jester

Designer: Unknown
Height: 6 ¾", 17.2 cm
Colour: Black, orange and green
Issued: Unknown

Name	Backstamp	U.S. $	Can. $	U.K. £
Jester	Green	1,100.00	1,250.00	750.00

Joan
Style One

Designer: Unknown
Height: 5", 12.7 cm
Colour: 1. Blue dress; blue hat with pink ribbon
2. Pink dress; green hat with pink ribbon
Issued: 1. c.1949 - 1972
2. 1973 - 1976
Series: Miniature Crinoline Lady

Colourways	Backstamp	U.S. $	Can. $	U.K. £
1. Blue dress	Green	400.00	475.00	265.00
2. Pink dress	Blue	400.00	475.00	265.00

Note: This is a reblocked figurine.

Judith Ann

Designer: Unknown
Height: 6 ½", 16.5 cm
Colour:
1. Blue-green dress; yellow shawl; blue-green hat with yellow ribbon
2. Burgundy dress; yellow shawl; yellow hat with blue ribbon
3. Green dress; brown shawl; green hat

Issued:
1. c.1949 - 1972
2. 1973 - 1976

Name	Backstamp	U.S. $	Can. $	U.K. £
1. Blue dress	Orange	250.00	300.00	175.00
2. Burgundy dress	Orange	250.00	300.00	175.00
3. Green dress	Orange	250.00	300.00	175.00

Note: This is a reblocked figurine. It probably exists with either a black or green backstamp.

June
Style One

Designer: Unknown
Height: 4 ½", 11.9 cm
Colour: Purple and green dress; lilac bonnet with green ribbon
Issued:
1. c.1949 - 1972
2. 1973 - 1976

Name	Backstamp	U.S. $	Can. $	U.K. £
1. June (Style One)	Black	325.00	400.00	225.00
2. June (Style One)	Orange	325.00	400.00	225.00

Note: This is a reblocked figurine. It probably exists with a green backstamp.

Kitty
Style One

Designer: Unknown
Height: 3 ½", 9.0 cm
Colour: Yellow dress; rose-pink bonnet with green ribbon
Issued:
1. c.1949 - 1972
2. 1973 - 1976

Series: Small Crinoline Lady

Name	Backstamp	U.S. $	Can. $	U.K. £
Kitty (Style One)	Blue	360.00	425.00	240.00

Note: This is a reblocked figurine. It probably exists with either a black or green backstamp.

Lady Bountiful

Designer: Unknown
Height: 6 ¾", 17.2 cm
Colour: Pink overskirt; green collar and underskirt; blue bows; pink bonnet with blue ribbon
Issued: c.1949 - 1972

Name	Backstamp	U.S. $	Can. $	U.K. £
Lady Bountiful	Green	435.00	500.00	290.00

Lady Rose
Style One

Designer: Unknown
Height: 6 ¾", 16.5 cm
Colour: Pink overskirt and bodice with purple flowers; green collar and underskirt; green bonnet with flowers and pink ribbon
Issued: c.1949 - 1972

Name	Backstamp	U.S. $	Can. $	U.K. £
Lady Rose (Style One)	Green	435.00	500.00	290.00

Lady with Borzoi

Designer: Unknown
Height: 6 ½", 16.7 cm
Colour: Yellow sweater; red skirt, scarf and hat; brown and white dog
Issued: c.1949 - 1972

Name	Backstamp	U.S. $	Can. $	U.K. £
Lady with Borzoi	Green	550.00	650.00	375.00

Maralyn

Designer: Unknown
Height: 6 ¼", 15.5 cm
Colour: Light green skirt, brown bodice; blue hat with red roses and bow
Issued: c.1949 - 1972

Name	Backstamp	U.S. $	Can. $	U.K. £
Maralyn	Green	475.00	550.00	325.00

Market Woman

Designer: Unknown
Height: 6", 15.0 cm
Colour: Yellow dress; white and blue checkered apron; green cloak; brown basket of flowers
Issued: c.1949 - 1972

Name	Backstamp	U.S. $	Can. $	U.K. £
Market Woman	Green	475.00	550.00	325.00

Medieval Lady

Designer: Unknown
Height: Unknown
Colour: Blue dress; burgundy cloak
Issued: c.1920

Name	Backstamp	U.S. $	Can. $	U.K. £
Medieval Lady	Black		Rare	

Minister (The)

Designer: Percy Simpson
Height: 5″, 12.7 cm
Colour: White and black robes; black bible and spectacles
Issued: c.1920
Series: The Bridal Party

Name	Backstamp	U.S. $	Can. $	U.K. £
Minister (The)	Black	375.00	425.00	250.00

Miss Julia

Designer: Unknown
Height: 6 ½″, 16.5 cm
Colour:
1. Pink dress with mauve overshirt; flowered yellow parasol
2. Pink dress with flowered mauve overskirt; yellow parasol

Issued: c.1920

Colourway	Backstamp	U.S. $	Can. $	U.K. £
1. Pink dress	Black	450.00	525.00	300.00
2. Pink flowered dress	Black	450.00	525.00	300.00

Miss Prudence

Designer: Unknown
Height: 6 ¾", 17.2 cm
Colour: Pale yellow and green dress, pink neckline; blue bonnet with pink ribbon; bouquet of flowers
Issued: c.1949 - 1972

Name	Backstamp	U.S. $	Can. $	U.K. £
Miss Prudence	Green	435.00	500.00	290.00

Mother of the Bride

Designer: Percy Simpson
Height: 5", 12.7 cm
Colour: Pale blue jacket; pink skirt and hat; black pince-nez
Issued: c.1920
Series: The Bridal Party

Name	Backstamp	U.S. $	Can. $	U.K. £
Mother of the Bride	Black	375.00	425.00	250.00

Orange Seller

Designer: Unknown
Height: 7 ¼", 18.4 cm
Colour: Pink and burgundy dress; dark green vest; brown basket of oranges
Issued: c.1949 - 1972

Name	Backstamp	U.S. $	Can. $	U.K. £
Orange Seller	Green	550.00	650.00	375.00

Pedlar

Designer: Unknown
Height: 6", 15.0 cm
Colour: Blue jacket; brown trouser and hat; green waistcoat; red neckerchief
Issued: c.1920

Name	Backstamp	U.S. $	Can. $	U.K. £
Pedlar	Black	550.00	650.00	375.00

Peggy

Designer: Unknown
Height: 4 ¾", 12.1 cm
Colour:
1. Rose-pink dress trimmed with blue; black bonnet with blue ribbon
2. Rose-pink dress trimmed with green; lilac bonnet with green ribbon

Issued: c.1949 - 1972

Colourways	Backstamp	U.S. $	Can. $	U.K. £
1. Pink/blue/black	Black	475.00	550.00	325.00
2. Pink/green/lilac	Green	475.00	550.00	325.00

Penelope
Style One

Designer: Unknown
Height: 6 ¼", 15.9 cm
Colour:
1. Beige dress with red roses; green underskirt; pink bonnet with green ribbon
2. Rose-pink dress; pale green, pink and yellow underskirt; black bonnet with green ribbon
3. Rose-pink dress; blue underskirt; black bonnet, blue ribbon
4. Turquoise dress

Issued:
1. c.1949 - 1972
2. 1975 - 1976

Name	Backstamp	U.S. $	Can. $	U.K. £
1. Penelope (Style One)	Black	390.00	450.00	260.00
2. Penelope (Style One)	Green	390.00	450.00	260.00
3. Penelope (Style One)	Orange	390.00	450.00	260.00

Note: This is a reblocked figurine.

Phyllis

Designer:	Unknown
Height:	3", 7.6 cm
Colour:	Brown and beige dress; brown hat
Issued:	1. c.1949 - 1972
	2. 1973 - 1976
Series:	Miniature Crinoline Lady

Name	Backstamp	U.S. $	Can. $	U.K. £
Phyllis	Blue	325.00	400.00	225.00

Note: This is a reblocked figurine. It probably exists with either a black or green backstamp.

Rosalinda

Designer:	Unknown
Height:	6 ¼", 15.9 cm
Colour:	1. Brown dress with white collar and frills; yellow purse; brown basket of flowers
	2. Green dress with pink collar and white frills; lilac-yellow basket of flowers
Issued:	1. c.1949 - 1972
	2. 1973 -1976

Name	Backstamp	U.S. $	Can. $	U.K. £
1. Rosalinda	Green	390.00	455.00	260.00
2. Rosalinda	Orange	390.00	455.00	260.00

Note: This is a reblocked figurine.

Spanish Lady

Designer:	Unknown
Height:	6 ¼", 15.9 cm
Colour:	1. Red, pink and blue dress - gloss
	2. Green - matte
Issued:	1. c.1949 - 1972
	2. 1974 - 1976

Colourways	Backstamp	U.S. $	Can. $	U.K. £
1. Gloss	Green	975.00	1,110.00	650.00
2. Matte	Green	975.00	1,110.00	650.00

Note: This is a reblocked figurine.

Strawberry Fayre
Style One

Designer: Unknown
Height: 6 ¾", 17.2 cm
Colour: Rose-pink dress, purple bodice; white apron; purple hat; brown basket of flowers
Issued: c.1949 - 1972

Name	Backstamp	U.S. $	Can. $	U.K. £
Strawberry Fayre	Green	550.00	650.00	375.00

Sylvia

Designer: Unknown
Height: 3 ¼", 8.2 cm
Colour: Rose-pink dress; rose-pink hat with yellow ribbon
Issued: 1. c.1949 - 1972
2. 1973 -1976
Series: Miniature Crinoline Lady

Name	Backstamp	U.S. $	Can. $	U.K. £
Sylvia	Blue	325.00	400.00	225.00

Note: This is a reblocked figurine.

Tinker

Designer:	Unknown
Height:	6 ¾", 17.2 cm
Colour:	1. Brown jacket; dark blue waistcoat; light brown trousers and hat; red neckerchief 2. Brown jacket; yellow waistcoat; light brown trousers and hat; red neckerchief
Issued:	1. c.1949 - 1972 2. 1974 - 1976

Name	Backstamp	U.S. $	Can. $	U.K. £
Tinker	Green	.00	.00	400.00

Note: This is a reblocked figurine.

COALPORT FIGURINES
1974 to date

The Roaring Twenties

Abigail
Style One

Designer: John Bromley
Modeller: John Bromley
Height: 7 ½", 19.1 cm
Colour: Dark blue and white dress; light brown dog
Issued: 1978 - 1982
Series: Ladies of Fashion

Name	U.S. $	Can. $	U.K. £
Abigail (Style One)	275.00	325.00	160.00

Abigail
Style Two

Designer: Unknown
Modeller: Martin Evans
Height: 3 ¾", 9.5 cm
Colour: Pale blue
Issued: 1995 to the present
Series: Minuettes

Name	U.S. $	Can. $	U.K. £
Abigail (Style Two)	55.00	89.50	30.00

Adele

Designer: John Bromley
Modeller: John Bromley
Height: 8 ¼", 21.0 cm
Colour: Blue
Issued: 1984
Varieties Also called Glenda; Melissa
Series: Ladies of Fashion

Name	U.S. $	Can. $	U.K. £
Adele	245.00	275.00	140.00

Note: Commissioned by Grattan Home Shopping.

Admiration

Designer:	John Bromley
Modeller:	John Bromley
Height:	7 ¼", 18.4 cm
Colour:	Pale green dress; tan cat
Issued:	1980 - 1988
Series:	Ladies of Fashion

Name	U.S. $	Can. $	U.K. £
Admiration	260.00	300.00	150.00

Affection

Designer:	John Bromley
Modeller:	John Bromley
Height:	8", 20.3 cm
Colour:	Rose-pink dress
Issued:	1977 - 1987
Series:	Ladies of Fashion

Name	U.S. $	Can. $	U.K. £
Affection	250.00	300.00	145.00

After Dark

Designer:	John Bromley
Modeller:	John Bromley
Height:	9", 22.5 cm
Colour:	Grey and black
Issued:	1989 - 1991
Series:	Ladies of Leisure

Name	U.S. $	Can. $	U.K. £
After Dark	300.00	350.00	175.00

After the Ball

Designer: John Bromley
Modeller: John Bromley
Height: 8", 20.3 cm
Colour: Lilac
Issued: 1983 - 1986
Series: Ladies of Fashion

Name	U.S. $	Can. $	U.K. £
After the Ball	275.00	325.00	160.00

Afternoon Matinee

Designer: Elizabeth Greenshields
Modeller: Brian Diment
Height: 8 ¼", 21.0 cm
Colour: Turquoise and lilac (porcelain)
Issued: 1991 - 1992
Series: Age of Elegance

Name	U.S. $	Can. $	U.K. £
Afternoon Matinee	300.00	350.00	180.00

Air

Designer: Sue Cashmore
Modeller: John Bromley
Height: 7 ¼", 18.4 cm
Colour: Pale blue
Issued: 1989 in a limited edition of 1,000
Series: The Elements

Name	U.S. $	Can. $	U.K. £
Air	400.00	475.00	235.00

Airman (R.A.F. 1945)

Designer:	John Bromley
Modeller:	John Bromley
Height:	8", 20.3 cm
Colour:	Navy
Issued:	1984 in a limited edition of 1,500
Series:	King and Country (1940 Period)

Name	U.S. $	Can. $	U.K. £
Airman (R.A.F. 1945)	350.00	400.00	195.00

Alexandra
Style One

Designer:	Helen Buckley
Modeller:	John Bromley
Height:	9", 22.9 cm
Clothing:	Unknown
Issued:	1987 - 1988
Series:	Somerset Collection

Name	U.S. $	Can. $	U.K. £
Alexandra (Style One)	275.00	325.00	160.00

Note: Alexandra is a porcelain figurine dressed in hand-sewn clothing. Prices are for figurine in mint condition with original clothing.

Photograph not available at press time

Alexandra
Style Two

Designer:	Martin Evans
Modeller:	Martin Evans
Height:	5 ¾", 14.6 cm
Colour:	Blue and beige (porcelain)
Issued:	1995 - 1997
Varieties:	Also called Jayne (Style Two)
Series:	Beau Monde

Name	U.S. $	Can. $	U.K. £
Alexandra (Style Two)	100.00	150.00	57.50

Alexandra at the Ball

Designer:	Shirley Curzon
Modeller:	John Bromley
Height:	8 ¼", 21.0 cm
Colour:	Pale lemon dress with white frills and black ribbon
Issued:	1988 in a limited edition of 12,500
Series:	Golden Age

Name	U.S. $	Can. $	U.K. £
Alexandra at the Ball	225.00	250.00	130.00

Note: Commissioned by Compton and Woodhouse.

Alexis

Designer:	John Bromley
Modeller:	John Bromley
Height:	8 ¼", 21.0 cm
Colour:	Sea-green
Issued:	1985 - 1987
Varieties:	Also called Felicity
Series:	Ladies of Fashion

Name	U.S. $	Can. $	U.K. £
Alexis	285.00	325.00	165.00

Alice

Designer:	John Bromley
Modeller:	John Bromley
Height:	8 ½", 21.6 cm
Colour:	Red and white
Issued:	1975 - 1980
Varieties:	Also called Fiona (Style One); Georgina (Style One)
Series:	Ladies of Fashion

Name	U.S. $	Can. $	U.K. £
Alice	325.00	375.00	185.00

Alison
Style One

Designer: John Bromley
Modeller: John Bromley
Height: 8 ½", 21.6 cm
Colour: Peach dress with white underskirt
Issued: Unknown, in a limited edition of 100
Varieties: Also called Emily; Flair; Heather (Style One); Henrietta
Series: Ladies of Fashion

Name	U.S. $	Can. $	U.K. £
Alison (Style One)	425.00	500.00	250.00

Note: Exclusive to Fenwick.

Alison
Style Two

Designer: John Bromley
Modeller: John Bromley
Height: 8", 20.3 cm
Colour: Red
Issued: 1995 - 1995
Series: Special Events

Name	U.S. $	Can. $	U.K. £
Alison (Style Two)	300.00	350.00	175.00

Allison

Designer: John Bromley
Modeller: John Bromley
Height: 8", 20.3 cm
Colour: Lilac and lavender
Issued: 1980 - 1982
Series: Ladies of Fashion

Name	U.S. $	Can. $	U.K. £
Allison	340.00	400.00	195.00

Amanda
Style One

Designer: John Bromley
Modeller: John Bromley
Height: 7 ½", 19.1 cm
Colour: Rose-pink dress with white neckline and sleeves; white hat with rose-pink ribbon
Issued: 1977 - 1991
Varieties: Also called Anna (Style One); Captivation; Teresa; Vanity Fayre
Series: Ladies of Fashion

Name	U.S. $	Can. $	U.K. £
Amanda (Style One)	250.00	290.00	145.00

Amanda
Style Two

Designer: Helen Buckley
Modeller: Andy Moss
Height: 4 ¾", 12.1 cm
Colour: Lavender
Issued: 1996 to the present
Series: Debutante Collection

Name	U.S. $	Can. $	U.K. £
Amanda (Style Two)	95.00	150.00	52.50

Amelia

Designer: Helen Buckley
Modeller John Bromley
Height: 9 ¾", 24.7 cm
Clothing: Burgundy velvet coat, hat and muff trimmed with fur
Issued: 1985 - 1988
Series: Somerset Collection

Name	U.S. $	Can. $	U.K. £
Amelia	425.00	500.00	225.00

Note: Amelia is a porcelain figurine dressed in hand-sewn clothing. Prices are for figurine in mint condition with original clothing.

Photograph not available at press time

Amy
Style One

Designer: John Bromley
Modeller: John Bromley
Height: Unknown
Colour: Unknown
Issued: 1985 - 1986
Series: Ladies of Fashion

Name	U.S. $	Can. $	U.K. £
Amy (Style One)	300.00	350.00	175.00

Note: Commissioned by Grattan Home Shopping.

Amy
Style Two

Designer: Unknown
Modeller: Martin Evans
Height: 4 ¾", 12.1 cm
Colour: Red
Issued: 1995 to the present
Varieties: Also called Eternity
Series: Debutante Collection

Name	U.S. $	Can. $	U.K. £
Amy (Style Two)	95.00	150.00	52.50

An Enchanted Evening

Designer: Unknown
Modeller: Unknown
Height: 9 ¼", 23.5 cm
Colour: Pink (porcelain)
Issued: 1995 - 1995
Series: When Dreams Come True

Name	U.S. $	Can. $	U.K. £
An Enchanted Evening	250.00	300.00	150.00

Note: Commissioned by the Danbury Mint.

Anastasia

Designer:	Elizabeth Greenshields
Modeller:	Brian Diment
Height:	5 ¼", 13.3 cm
Colour:	Yellow and orange (porcelain)
Issued:	1993 - 1994
Series:	Beau Monde

Name	U.S. $	Can. $	U.K. £
Anastasia	165.00	190.00	95.00

Andrea

Designer:	John Bromley
Modeller:	John Bromley
Height:	5", 12.7 cm
Colour:	Peach
Issued:	1983 - 1989
Varieties:	Also called Claire (Style One); Maxine; Pamela (Style One); Susan (Style One)
Series:	Debutante Collection

Name	U.S. $	Can. $	U.K. £
Andrea	165.00	190.00	95.00

Angela

Designer:	Elizabeth Greenshields
Modeller:	Brian Diment
Height:	5 ½", 14.0 cm
Colour:	Pale green (porcelain)
Issued:	1994 to the present
Series	Beau Monde

Name	U.S. $	Can. $	U.K. £
Angela	100.00	175.00	57.50

Photograph not available at press time

Angelica

Designer:	John Bromley
Modeller:	John Bromley
Height:	Unknown
Colour:	Unknown
Issued:	1987 in a limited edition of 250
Series:	Edwardian Beauties

Name	U.S. $	Can. $	U.K. £
Angelica	300.00	350.00	175.00

Angelique

Designer:	John Bromley
Modeller:	John Bromley
Height:	6 ½", 15.9 cm
Colour:	Green dress; cream underskirt with green stars
Issued:	1975 - 1982
Varieties:	Also called Celeste; Joy
Series:	Ladies of Fashion

Name	U.S. $	Can. $	U.K. £
Angelique	280.00	325.00	160.00

Anita

Designer:	John Bromley
Modeller:	John Bromley
Height:	5", 12.7 cm
Colour:	Green and purple
Issued:	1992 to the present
Series:	Debutante Collection

Name	U.S. $	Can. $	U.K. £
Anita	100.00	150.00	52.50

Ann

Designer: John Bromley
Modeller: John Bromley
Height: 5", 12.7 cm
Colour: Blue
Issued: 1988 - 1993
Series: Debutante Collection

Name	U.S. $	Can. $	U.K. £
Ann	130.00	150.00	75.00

Anna
Style One

Designer: John Bromley
Modeller: John Bromley
Height: 7 ½", 19.1 cm
Colour: Bright red dress, grey trim neckline and sleeves; grey hat with red ribbon
Issued: 1985 - 1985
Varieties: Also called Amanda (Style One); Captivation; Teresa; Vanity Fayre
Series: Ladies of Fashion

Name	U.S. $	Can. $	U.K. £
Anna (Style One)	315.00	360.00	180.00

Note: Commissioned by Grattan Home Shopping.

Anna
Style Two

Designer: Helen Buckley
Modeller: John Bromley
Height: 7 ¾", 19.7 cm
Colour: White dress with gold highlights
Issued: 1991 - 1993
Varieties: Also called Special Memories
Series: Grosvenor Collection

Name	U.S. $	Can. $	U.K.
Anna (Style Two)	300.00	350.00	175.00

Annabelle
Style One

Designer: John Bromley
Modeller: John Bromley
Height: 8 ½", 21.6 cm
Colour: Yellow and peach
Issued: 1975 - 1982
Varieties: Also called Lucy (Style One); Sarah (Style One)
Series: Ladies of Fashion

Name	U.S. $	Can. $	U.K. £
Annabelle (Style One)	280.00	325.00	160.00

Annabelle
Style Two

Designer: Unknown
Modeller: Unknown
Height: 7 ¾", 19.7 cm
Colour: Blue
Issued: 1997 to the present
Varieties: Also called Belinda
Series: Ladies of Fashion

Name	U.S. $	Can. $	U.K. £
Annabelle (Style Two)	160.00	180.00	89.99

Note: Commissioned by G.U.S. Home Shopping.

Anne
Style One

Designer: John Bromley
Modeller: John Bromley
Height: 7 ½", 19.1 cm
Colour: Gold
Issued: 1975 - 1977
Varieties: Also called Dianne; Sophia (Style One)
Series: Ladies of Fashion

Name	U.S. $	Can. $	U.K. £
Anne	300.00	350.00	175.00

Anne
Style Two

Designer:	John Bromley
Modeller:	John Bromley
Height:	8 ½", 21.6 cm
Colour:	Black jacket, cap and boots; yellow breeches
Issued:	1980 - 1980

Name	U.S. $	Can. $	U.K. £
Anne (Style Two)	300.00	350.00	175.00

Anne
Style Three

Designer:	Helen Buckley
Modeller:	Jack Glynn
Height:	8", 20.3 cm
Colour:	Blue
Issued:	1997 - 1997
Series:	Ladies of Fashion Figure of the Year

Name	U.S. $	Can. $	U.K. £
Anne (Style Three)	175.00	295.00	100.00

Anne Boleyn

Designer:	Unknown
Modeller:	Robert Worthington
Height:	8", 20.3 cm
Colour:	Peach, orange and grey
Issued:	1979 - 1992
Series:	Royal Collection

Name	U.S. $	Can. $	U.K. £
Anne Boleyn	550.00	650.00	325.00

Anne Marie

Designer: John Bromley
Modeller: John Bromley
Height: 7 ½", 19.1 cm
Colour: Tan skirt and hat; cream top with tan spots
Issued: 1975 - 1977
Varieties: Also called Julie (Style One); Louise
Series: Ladies of Fashion

Name	U.S. $	Can. $	U.K. £
Anne Marie	285.00	325.00	165.00

Anne of Cleves

Designer: Unknown
Modeller: Robert Worthington
Height: 8", 20.3 cm
Colour: Red and rose-pink
Issued: 1979 - 1992
Series: Royal Collection

Name	U.S. $	Can. $	U.K. £
Anne of Cleves	575.00	625.00	325.00

Anne of Green Gables
Variation One

Designer: John Bromley
Modeller: John Bromley
Height: 8 ½" 21.6 cm
Colour: Purple dress; white apron (matte)
Issued: 1982 in a limited edition of 2,500

Name	U.S. $	Can. $	U.K. £
Anne of Green Gables (Variation One)	385.00	440.00	220.00

Note: Commissioned by Canadian Collector Plates, Milliken, Ontario. Original issue price $235.00.

Anne of Green Gables
Variation Two

Designer: John Bromley
Modeller: John Bromley
Height: 8 ½", 21.6 cm
Colour: Green and white (matte)
Issued: 1997 in a limited edition of 2,500

Name	U.S. $	Can. $	U.K. £
Anne of Green Gables (Variation Two)	N/A	260.00	N/A

Note: Commissioned exclusively for the Canadian market. These figurines are not individually numbered.

Photograph not available at press time

Annette
Style Three

Designer: Unknown
Modeller: Unknown
Height: Unknown
Colour: Unknown
Issued: 1982 - 1983
Series: Little Women

Name	U.S. $	Can. $	U.K. £
Annette (Style Three)	215.00	250.00	125.00

Annette
Style Four

Designer: John Bromley
Modeller: John Bromley
Height: 5", 12.5 cm
Colour: Pale yellow and pink
Issued: 1982 - 1985
Varieties: Also called Claudette (Style Two); Jeanette (Style Two); Joanne (Style Two); Juliette (Style Two); Lynette (Style Two); Sally Anne (Style One)
Series: Debutante Collection

Name	U.S. $	Can. $	U.K. £
Annette (Style Four)	165.00	190.00	95.00

Anthea
Style One

Designer:	Helen Buckley
Modeller:	John Bromley
Height:	7 ¾", 19.7 cm
Colour:	Peach
Issued:	1986 - 1989
Series:	Ladies of Fashion

Name	U.S. $	Can. $	U.K. £
Anthea (Style One)	300.00	345.00	175.00

Anthea
Style Two

Designer:	John Bromley
Modeller:	John Bromley
Height:	8", 20.3 cm
Colour:	Pink and white (porcelain)
Issued:	1997
Varieties:	Also called Leona; Louisa
Series:	Ladies of Fashion

Name	U.S. $	Can. $	U.K. £
Anthea (Style Two)	235.00	275.00	135.00

Note: Commissioned by Littlewoods Home Shopping.

Antonia
Style One

Designer:	John Bromley
Modeller:	John Bromley
Height:	8 ½", 21.6 cm
Colour:	Light brown and cream
Issued:	1984 - 1988
Varieties:	Also called Enchantress; Marjorie
Series:	Ladies of Fashion

Name	U.S. $	Can. $	U.K. £
Antonia (Style One)	285.00	325.00	165.00

Antonia
Style Two

Designer: John Bromley
Height: 8 ½", 21.6 cm
Colour: Burgundy with gold highlights
Issued: 1996
Varieties: Also called Evening at the Opera
Series: Ladies of Fashion

Name	U.S. $	Can. $	U.K. £
Antonia (Style Two)	175.00	200.00	99.95

Note: Commissioned by Littlewoods Home Shopping.

Antony

Designer: Robert Worthington
Height: 10 ½", 26.7 cm
Colour: Burgundy, gold and brown
Issued: 1981 - 1982
Series: Characters from Shakespeare

Name	U.S. $	Can. $	U.K. £
Antony	425.00	500.00	250.00

Apple Girl (The)

Designer: John Bromley
Height: 8", 20.3 cm
Colour: Burgundy and pink dress; white dog
Issued: 1985 in a limited edition of 1,000
Series: Arcadian Collection

Name	U.S. $	Can. $	U.K. £
Apple Girl (The)	340.00	400.00	195.00

Apple Woman

Designer:	Robert Worthington
Height:	8", 20.3 cm
Colour:	Yellow skirt; red jacket and cape; white apron; basket of apples
Issued:	1982 - 1985
Series:	Character Collection

Name	U.S. $	Can. $	U.K. £
Apple Woman	300.00	350.00	175.00

April

Designer:	John Bromley
Height:	5", 12.7 cm
Colour:	Yellow
Issued:	1993 - 1997
Varieties:	Also called Poppy (Style One)
Series:	Debutante Collection

Name	U.S. $	Can. $	U.K.£
April	100.00	160.00	52.50

Arabella

Designer:	Helen Buckley
Modeller:	John Bromley
Height:	9 ½", 24.0 cm
Clothing:	Green velvet coat, skirt and hat trimmed with lace
Issued:	1985 - 1988
Series:	Somerset Collection

Name	U.S. $	Can. $	U.K. £
Arabella	385.00	440.00	220.00

Note: Arabella is a porcelain figurine dressed in hand-sewn clothing. Prices are for figurine in mint condition with original clothing.

Ascot Lady, 1984 (The)

Designer: David Shilling
Modeller: John Bromley
Height: 8 ¼", 21.0 cm
Colour: Pink
Issued: 1984 in a limited edition of 750
Series: Ascot Ladies

Name	U.S. $	Can. $	U.K. £
Ascot Lady, 1984 (The)	425.00	500.00	250.00

Ascot Lady, 1985 (The)

Designer: David Shilling
Modeller: John Bromley
Height: 9", 22.9 cm
Colour: Pink
Issued: 1985 in a limited edition of 750
Series: Ascot Ladies

Name	U.S. $	Can. $	U.K. £
Ascot Lady, 1985 (The)	425.00	500.00	250.00

Ascot Lady, 1986 (The)

Designer: David Shilling
Modeller: John Bromley
Height: 8 ¼", 21.0 cm
Colour: Purple and white
Issued: 1986 in a limited edition of 750
Series: Ascot Ladies

Name	U.S. $	Can. $	U.K. £
Ascot Lady, 1986 (The)	425.00	500.00	250.00

Ascot Lady, 1987 (The)

Designer:	David Shilling
Modeller:	John Bromley
Height:	8 ½", 21.6 cm
Colour:	Yellow and lilac
Issued:	1987 in a limited edition of 750
Series:	Ascot Ladies

Name	U.S. $	Can. $	U.K. £
Ascot Lady, 1987 (The)	475.00	550.00	275.00

Ascot Lady, 1988 (The)

Designer:	David Shilling
Modeller:	John Bromley
Height:	8 ¼", 21.0 cm
Colour:	Peach and gold
Issued:	1988 in a limited edition of 750
Series:	Ascot Ladies

Name	U.S. $	Can. $	U.K. £
Ascot Lady, 1988 (The)	465.00	525.00	265.00

Ascot Lady, 1989 (The)

Designer:	David Shilling
Modeller:	John Bromley
Height:	8 ¾", 22.2 cm
Colour:	Green
Issued:	1989 in a limited edition of 750
Series:	Ascot Ladies

Name	U.S. $	Can. $	U.K. £
Ascot Lady, 1989 (The)	425.00	500.00	250.00

Ashley

Designer:	Unknown
Height:	8 ¼", 21.0 cm
Colour:	1. Rose-pink dress and hat; grey shawl and parasol
	2. Pale pink dress and hat; white shawl and parasol
Issued:	1987 - 1991
Series:	Ladies of Fashion

Name	U.S. $	Can. $	U.K. £
Ashley	285.00	325.00	165.00

Attraction

Designer:	Elizabeth Greenshields
Modeller:	John Bromley
Height:	7 ¼", 18.4 cm
Colour:	White dress with gold highlights
Issued:	1991 - 1992
Varieties:	Also called Chloe (Style Two); Demure; Julia (Style Two)
Series:	Chantilly Lace

Name	U.S. $	Can. $	U.K. £
Attraction	280.00	375.00	160.00

Auguste's Bouquet

Designer:	Michael Abberley
Modeller:	John Bromley
Height:	8 ½", 22.2 cm
Colour:	Yellow, red, green and blue
Issued:	1986 - 1988
Series:	Cavalcade of Clowns

Name	U.S. $	Can. $	U.K. £
Auguste's Bouquet	340.00	400.00	195.00

Auguste's Mishap

Designer: Michael Abberley
Modeller: John Bromley
Height: 7 ½", 18.4 cm
Colour: Cream, green, red and yellow
Issued: 1986 - 1988
Series: Cavalcade of Clowns

Name	U.S. $	Can. $	U.K. £
Auguste's Mishap	340.00	400.00	195.00

Autumn Grace

Designer: John Bromley
Height: Unknown
Colour: Unknown
Issued: 1984 - 1986
Series: Ladies of Fashion

Name	U.S. $	Can. $	U.K. £
Autumn Grace	280.00	325.00	160.00

Photograph not available at press time

Autumn Leaves

Designer: John Bromley
Height: 7 ½", 21.0 cm
Colour: Brown, blue and green
Issued: 1982 in a limited edition of 750
Series: Four Seasons

Name	U.S. $	Can. $	U.K. £
Autumn Leaves	340.00	400.00	195.00

Autumn Stroll

Designer:	Elizabeth Greenshields
Modeller:	Unknown
Height:	8 ½", 21.6 cm
Colour:	Cream and brown (porcelain)
Issued:	1993 - 1996
Series:	Age of Elegance

Name	U.S. $	Can. $	U.K. £
Autumn Stroll	350.00	425.00	175.00

Ball (The)

Designer:	John Bromley
Modeller:	John Bromley
Height:	7", 17.8 cm
Colour:	White with gold trim
Issued:	1977 - 1987
Varieties:	Also called Madeline
Series:	Ladies of Fashion

Name	U.S. $	Can. $	U.K. £
Ball (The)	285.00	325.00	165.00

Barbara Ann

Designer:	Helen Buckley
Modeller:	John Bromley
Height:	8 ¼", 21.0 cm
Colour:	Pink and purple
Issued:	1988 to the present
Series:	Ladies of Fashion

Name	U.S. $	Can. $	U.K. £
Barbara Ann	350.00	585.00	175.00

Basket Maker (The)

Designer:	Margaret Whittaker
Height:	7 ¼", 18.4 cm
Colour:	Browns and green (matt)
Issued:	1974 in a limited edition of 1,000
Series:	Craft Figures

Name	U.S. $	Can. $	U.K. £
Basket Maker (The)	300.00	350.00	175.00

Beatrice
Style One

Designer:	John Bromley
Height:	5 ¼", 13.3 cm
Colour:	Light green
Issued:	1985 - 1986
Varieties:	Also called Hannah (Style One); Prudence
Series:	Debutante Collection

Name	U.S. $	Can. $	U.K. £
Beatrice (Style One)	195.00	220.00	110.00

Beatrice
Style Two

Designer:	Helen Buckley
Modeller:	Andy Moss
Height:	4 ¼", 10.8 cm
Colour:	Sea-green and mauve (porcelain)
Issued:	1997 to the present
Series:	Beau Monde

Name	U.S. $	Can. $	U.K. £
Beatrice (Style Two)	100.00	175.00	57.50

Beatrice at the Garden Party

Designer:	Shirley Curzon
Modeller:	John Bromley
Height:	8 ¼", 21.0 cm
Colour:	Pale blue dress with slate blue trim; pink rose on pale blue hat
Issued:	1989 in a limited edition of 12,500
Series:	Golden Age

Name	U.S. $	Can. $	U.K. £
Beatrice at the Garden Party	225.00	260.00	130.00

Note: Commissioned by Compton and Woodhouse.

Becky

Designer:	John Bromley
Height:	5", 12.7 cm
Colour:	Pink and peach
Issued:	1990 - 1993
Series:	Debutante Collection

Name	U.S. $	Can. $	U.K. £
Becky	130.00	150.00	75.00

Bedtime Story

Designer:	David Shilling
Modeller:	John Bromley
Height:	8", 20.3 cm
Colour:	Pale pink, yellow, mauve and green
Issued:	1986 in a limited edition of 1,000
Series:	Designer Series

Name	U.S. $	Can. $	U.K. £
Bedtime Story	395.00	450.00	225.00

Belinda

Designer: Unknown
Height: 7 ¾", 19.7 cm
Colour: Rose-pink
Issued: 1993 to the present
Varieties: Also called Annabelle (Style Two)
Series: Ladies of Fashion

Name	U.S. $	Can. $	U.K. £
Belinda	235.00	260.00	135.00

Belle of the Ball
Style One

Designer: Val Littlewood
Modeller: John Bromley
Height: 9 ¼", 23.5 cm
Colour: Peach and white
Issued: 1989 - 1991
Series: Ladies of Leisure

Name	U.S. $	Can. $	U.K. £
Belle of the Ball (Style One)	300.00	350.00	175.00

Belle of the Ball
Style Two

Designer: John Bromley
Modeller: John Bromley
Height: 9 ½", 24.0 cm
Colour: Pink
Issued: 1996 in a limited edition of 1,000
Series: Park Lane Collection

Name	U.S. $	Can. $	U.K. £
Belle of the Ball (Style Two)	175.00	200.00	100.00

Berenice

Designer:	Unknown
Modeller:	Martin Evans
Height:	5 ¼", 13.3 cm
Colour:	Peach and black (porcelain)
Issued:	1993 to the present
Series:	Beau Monde

Name	U.S. $	Can. $	U.K. £
Berenice	100.00	235.00	57.50

Best Friend

Designer:	Unknown
Modeller:	Sheila Mitchell
Height:	6 ¼", 15.5 cm
Colour:	Blue, white and brown
Issued:	1989 in a limited edition of 12,500
Series:	R.S.P.C.A.

Name	U.S. $	Can. $	U.K. £
Best Friend	265.00	300.00	150.00

Note: Commissioned by Compton and Woodhouse and issued to commemorate the 150th anniversary of the R.S.P.C.A.

Beth

Designer:	Helen Buckley
Modeller:	Jack Glynn
Height:	4", 10.1 cm
Colour:	Peach and yellow
Issued:	1996 to the present
Series:	Debutante Collection

Name	U.S. $	Can. $	U.K. £
Beth	100.00	150.00	52.50

Bethan

Designer:	John Bromley
Height:	8", 20.3 cm
Colour:	Purple
Issued:	1996 in a limited edition of 250
Varieties:	Also called Twenty-One Today
Series:	Welsh Ladies of Fashion

Name	U.S. $	Can. $	U.K. £
Bethan	200.00	230.00	115.00

Note: Commissioned by J. T. Morgan & Co. Ltd., Wales.

Beverley

Designer:	John Bromley
Height:	8", 20.3 cm
Colour:	Unknown
Issued:	1984 - 1986
Series:	Ladies of Fashion

Name	U.S. $	Can. $	U.K. £
Beverley	260.00	300.00	150.00

Note: Commissioned by Grattan Home Shopping.

Photograph not available at press time

Bewitching

Designer:	John Bromley
Height:	8 ½", 21.6 cm
Colour:	Burgundy and blue
Issued:	1991 - 1994
Series:	Ladies of Fashion

Name	U.S. $	Can. $	U.K. £
Bewitching	340.00	400.00	195.00

Birthday Girl (The)

Designer: John Bromley
Modeller: John Bromley
Height: 8", 20.3 cm
Colour: Blue-green and white
Issued: 1989 - 1990
Series: Ladies of Fashion

Name	U.S. $	Can. $	U.K. £
Birthday Girl (The)	285.00	325.00	165.00

Blacksmith (The)

Designer: Margaret Whittaker
Height: Unknown
Colour: Brown
Issued: 1974 in a limited edition of 1,000
Series: Craft Figures

Name	U.S. $	Can. $	U.K. £
Blacksmith (The)	300.00	350.00	175.00

Blanche
Style One

Designer: John Bromley
Modeller: John Bromley
Height: 7 ½", 19.1 cm
Colour: Flowered green dress
Issued: 1975 - 1980
Varieties: Also called Collette; Rosemary (Style One)
Series: Ladies of Fashion

Name	U.S. $	Can. $	U.K. £
Blanche (Style One)	300.00	350.00	175.00

Blanche
Style Two

Designer:	Andrea Cox
Modeller:	Jack Glynn
Height:	12", 30.5 cm
Colour:	Lemon dress; orange coat with brown fur trim
Issued:	1997 to the present
Series:	The Roaring Twenties (Style Two)

Name	U.S. $	Can. $	U.K. £
Blanche (Style Two)	215.00	485.00	125.00

Blenheim Park

Designer:	Elizabeth Greenshields
Modeller:	Brian Diment
Height:	8 ¼", 21.0 cm
Colour:	Blue and lavender (porcelain)
Issued:	1993 - 1995
Series:	Age of Elegance

Name	U.S. $	Can. $	U.K. £
Blenheim Park	325.00	425.00	165.00

Blue Moon

Designer:	John Bromley
Height:	8", 20.3 cm
Colour:	Purple
Issued:	1996 in a limited edition of 1,000
Series:	English Rose

Name	U.S. $	Can. $	U.K. £
Blue Moon	400.00	575.00	200.00

Boating Party

Designer:	David Shilling
Modeller:	John Bromley
Height:	8 ½", 21.6 cm
Colour:	White, blue and gold
Issued:	1989 in a limited edition of 1,000
Series:	Romance of Henley

Name	U.S. $	Can. $	U.K. £
Boating Party	395.00	450.00	225.00

Bobbie

Designer:	Unknown
Height:	7 ¾", 19.7 cm
Colour:	White dress with gold highlights
Issued:	1991 - 1992
Series:	Roaring Twenties (Style One)

Name	U.S. $	Can. $	U.K. £
Bobbie	300.00	350.00	175.00

Bolero

Designer:	Helen Buckley
Modeller:	John Bromley
Height:	7 ¾", 19.7 cm
Colour:	Lavender and white
Issued:	1990 - 1995
Varieties:	Also called Fleur
Series:	Ladies of Fashion

Name	U.S. $	Can. $	U.K. £
Bolero	285.00	330.00	165.00

Bonnie Lass

Designer: John Bromley
Height: 4 ¾", 12.1 cm
Colour: Blue, green and pink
Issued: 1989 - 1994
Series: Debutante Collection

Name	U.S. $	Can. $	U.K. £
Bonnie Lass	165.00	190.00	95.00

Boy (The)

Designer: Elizabeth Woodhouse
Modeller: Sheila Mitchell
Height: 7 ¼", 18.4 cm
Colour: Blue and brown
Issued: 1988 in a limited edition of 9,500
Series: National Childrens Home

Name	U.S. $	Can. $	U.K. £
Boy (The)	265.00	300.00	150.00

Note: Commissioned by Compton and Woodhouse and issued to commemorate 120 years of the National Childrens Home.

Boy Boating

Designer: Pauline Shone
Height: 6 ¾", 17.2 cm
Colour: White shirt; blue dungarees; blue and white sailboat
Issued: 1979 - unknown
Series: Children Studies

Name	U.S. $	Can. $	U.K. £
Boy Boating	265.00	300.00	150.00

Boy Climbing Tree

Designer: Pauline Shone
Height: Unknown
Colour: Unknown
Issued: 1979 - unknown
Series: Children Studies

Name	U.S. $	Can. $	U.K. £
Boy Climbing Tree	265.00	300.00	150.00

Photograph not available at press time

Note: Original issue price £48.50.

Boy Fishing

Designer: Pauline Shone
Height: 7 ¼", 18.4 cm
Colour: Pale blue shirt; white trousers
Issued: 1979 - unknown
Series: Children Studies

Name	U.S. $	Can. $	U.K. £
Boy Fishing	265.00	300.00	150.00

Boy With Bird

Designer: Alan E. Harmer
Height: Unknown
Colour: White, red and black
Issued: 1979 - unknown
Series: Japanese Studies

Name	U.S. $	Can. $	U.K. £
Boy With Bird	340.00	400.00	195.00

Boy With Butterfly

Designer:	Alan E. Harmer
Height:	Unknown
Colour:	White, red and black
Issued:	1979 - unknown
Series:	Japanese Studies

Name	U.S. $	Can. $	U.K. £
Boy With Butterfly	340.00	400.00	195.00

Breeze
Style Two

Designer:	Elizabeth Greenshields
Modeller:	John Bromley
Height:	7 ¼", 18.4 cm
Colour:	White and yellow dress with gold highlights
Issued:	1991 - 1993
Varieties:	Also called Graceful
Series:	Chantilly Lace

Name	U.S. $	Can. $	U.K. £
Breeze (Style Two)	285.00	325.00	165.00

Photograph not available at press time

Brenda

Designer:	John Bromley
Height:	Unknown
Colour:	Unknown
Issued:	1986 - unknown
Series:	Ladies of Fashion

Name	U.S. $	Can. $	U.K. £
Brenda	265.00	350.00	175.00

Bride (The)
Style Two

Designer: John Bromley
Modeller: John Bromley
Height: 8", 20.3 cm
Colour: White dress; red rose bouquet
Issued: 1981 - 1986
Series: Brides

Name	U.S. $	Can. $	U.K. £
Bride (Style Two)	285.00	325.00	165.00

Bridesmaid
Style Three

Designer: Pauline Shone
Height: 9 ½", 24.0 cm
Colour: White dress with pink ribbon; pink rose bouquet
Issued: 1979 - unknown
Series: Children Studies

Name	U.S. $	Can. $	U.K. £
Bridesmaid (Style Three)	215.00	250.00	125.00

Note: Original issue price £29.00.

Bridesmaid
Style Four

Designer: John Bromley
Height: 6", 15.0 cm
Colour: Lemon
Issued: 1981 - 1984
Varieties: Also called Flower Girl (Style One)
Series: Ladies of Fashion

Name	U.S. $	Can. $	U.K. £
Bridesmaid (Style Four)	215.00	250.00	125.00

Bridesmaid
Style Five

Designer:	Unknown
Height:	6", 15.0 cm
Colour:	Pink dress with white underskirt; red rose bouquet
Issued:	1992 in a limited edition of 1,500
Series:	Wedding Collection

Name	U.S. $	Can. $	U.K. £
Bridesmaid (Style Five)	245.00	280.00	140.00

Bridget

Designer:	John Bromley
Height:	8 ½", 21.6 cm
Colour:	Blue and beige
Issued:	1992 - 1997
Series:	Ladies of Fashion

Name	U.S. $	Can. $	U.K. £
Bridget	175.00	325.00	110.00

Brighton Promenade

Designer:	Glenis Devereaux
Modeller:	Glenis Devereaux
Height:	8 ¾", 22.2 cm
Colour:	Pale green and pink (porcelain)
Issued:	1996 to the present
Series:	Age of Elegance

Name	U.S. $	Can. $	U.K. £
Brighton Promenade	225.00	395.00	130.00

Britannia

Designer:	Unknown
Height:	11 ½", 29.2cm
Colour:	White robes; gold helmet; brown lion
Issued:	1986 - 1987
Series:	Romance and Legend

Name	U.S. $	Can. $	U.K. £
Britannia	1,100.00	1,300.00	650.00

Butterflies

Designer:	Shiela Mitchell
Height:	7 ½", 19.1 cm
Colour:	1. Flesh tones; pale pink ballet dress
	2. All white
Issued:	1. 1990 in a limited edition of 9,500
	2. 1990 in a limited edition of 9,500
Series:	The Ballet Shoes Collection

Colour	U.S. $	Can. $	U.K. £
1. Flesh tones	175.00	200.00	100.00
2. White	130.00	150.00	75.00

Note: Commissioned by Compton and Woodhouse.

Buckingham Palace Guard

Designer:	Margaret Whittaker
Modeller:	Robert Worthington
Height:	10 ½", 26.7 cm
Colour:	Red tunic; black trousers
Issued:	1980 - 1985
Series:	London Heritage

Name	U.S. $	Can. $	U.K. £
Buckingham Palace Guard	300.00	350.00	175.00

Cafe Royal

Designer:	Helen Buckley
Modeller:	John Bromley
Height:	8 ¼", 21.0 cm
Colour:	Pale peach
Issued:	1991 - 1997
Varieties:	Also called Donna (Style Two)
Series:	Ladies of Fashion

Name	U.S. $	Can. $	U.K. £
Cafe Royal	250.00	425.00	130.00

Camilla

Designer:	John Bromley
Modeller:	John Bromley
Height:	8", 20.3 cm
Colour:	Purple and pale blue
Issued:	1992 - 1996
Series:	Ladies of Fashion

Name	U.S. $	Can. $	U.K. £
Camilla	250.00	325.00	145.00

Candida

Designer:	John Bromley
Modeller:	John Bromley
Height:	8 ½", 21.6 cm
Colour:	1. Dark green dress; yellow blouse; pink and yellow hat 2. Gold and yellow
Issued:	1976 - 1980
Varieties:	Also called Rebecca (Style One); Roberta
Series:	Ladies of Fashion

Name	U.S. $	Can. $	U.K. £
1. Dark green	300.00	350.00	175.00
2. Gold and yellow	300.00	350.00	175.00

Captivation

Designer: John Bromley
Modeller: John Bromley
Height: 7 ½", 19.1 cm
Colour: Brown
Issued: 1984 - 1986
Varieties: Also called Amanda (Style One); Anna (Style One); Teresa; Vanity Fayre
Series: Ladies of Fashion

Name	U.S. $	Can. $	U.K. £
Captivation	285.00	325.00	165.00

Caress

Designer: Elizabeth Greenshields
Modeller: John Bromley
Height: 7 ¼", 18.4 cm
Colour: Pink
Issued: 1992 - 1993
Varieties: Also called Glamour
Series: Chantilly Lace

Name	U.S. $	Can. $	U.K. £
Caress	280.00	325.00	160.00

Carla

Designer: John Bromley
Modeller: John Bromley
Height: 5 ¼", 13.3 cm
Colour: Light green dress; white hat
Issued: 1987 - 1992
Varieties: Also called Catriona; Penny
Series: Debutante Collection

Name	U.S. $	Can. $	U.K. £
Carla	130.00	150.00	75.00

Carnation

Designer:	Jack Glynn
Height:	9", 22.9 cm
Colour:	Pink crinoline gown and hat; bouquet of carnations
Issued:	1994 in a limited edition of 12,500
Series:	The Four Flowers Collection

Name	U.S. $	Can. $	U.K. £
Carnation	280.00	320.00	160.00

Note: Commissioned by Compton and Woodhouse.

Carnival

Designer:	Helen Buckley
Modeller:	John Bromley
Height:	8 ¼", 21.1 cm
Colour:	Cream and pink
Issued:	1991 - 1994
Series:	Ladies of Fashion

Name	U.S. $	Can. $	U.K.
Carnival	285.00	350.00	165.00

Carol
Style Two

Designer:	John Bromley
Modeller:	John Bromley
Height:	6 ½", 16.5 cm
Colour:	Rose-pink and pale pink
Issued:	1984 - 1987
Series:	Ladies of Fashion

Name	U.S. $	Can. $	U.K. £
Carol (Style Two)	300.00	350.00	175.00

Carole

Designer: Graham Miller
Height: 10", 25.4 cm
Colour: Pale blue
Issued: 1993 to the present
Varieties: Also called Sally
Series: Silhouettes

Name	U.S. $	Can. $	U.K. £
Carole	130.00	235.00	72.50

Caroline
Style One

Designer: John Bromley
Modeller: John Bromley
Height: 8", 20.3 cm
Colour: Red dress with white frills
Issued: 1979 - 1988
Series: Ladies of Fashion

Name	U.S. $	Can. $	U.K. £
Caroline (Style One)	285.00	325.00	165.00

Caroline
Style Two

Designer: Unknown
Modeller: Jack Glynn
Height: 5 ¼", 13.3 cm
Colour: Lavender
Issued: 1994 - 1996
Series: Debutante Collection

Name	U.S. $	Can. $	U.K. £
Caroline (Style Two)	100.00	120.00	60.00

Carrie

Designer: John Bromley
Modeller: John Bromley
Height: 5", 12.7 cm
Colour: Pink and purple
Issued: 1991 - 1993
Varieties: Also called Encore
Series: Debutante Collection

Name	U.S. $	Can. $	U.K. £
Carrie	130.00	150.00	75.00

Cassie

Designer: John Bromley
Modeller: John Bromley
Height: 5", 12.7 cm
Colour: Purple
Issued: 1988 - 1994
Series: Debutante Collection

Name	U.S. $	Can. $	U.K. £
Cassie	130.00	150.00	75.00

Catherine
Style One

Designer: Helen Buckley
Modeller: John Bromley
Height: 9 ¾", 24.7 cm
Clothing: White silk dress with pink flowers and blue bows trimmed with lace
Issued: 1985 - 1988
Series: Somerset Collection

Name	U.S. $	Can. $	U.K. £
Catherine (Style One)	340.00	400.00	195.00

Note: Catherine is a porcelain figurine dressed in hand-sewn clothing. Prices are for figurine in mint condition with original clothing.

Catherine
Style Two

Designer: Helen Buckley
Modeller: Jack Glynn
Height: 8 ¼", 21.0 cm
Colour: Pale blue
Issued: 1997 - 1997
Series: Collingwood Collection (Membership exclusive)

Name	U.S. $	Can. $	U.K. £
Catherine (Style Two)	160.00	250.00	90.00

Catherine of Aragon

Designer: Robert Worthington
Height: 8", 20.3 cm
Colour: Dark blue and brown
Issued: 1979 - 1992
Series: Royal Collection

Name	U.S. $	Can. $	U.K. £
Catherine of Aragon	550.00	575.00	325.00

Catherine Parr

Designer: Robert Worthington
Height: 8", 20.3 cm
Colour: Green, rose-pink and brown
Issued: 1979 - 1992
Series: Royal Collection

Name	U.S. $	Can. $	U.K. £
Catherine Parr	550.00	675.00	325.00

Catherine The Great of Russia

Designer: John Bromley
Modeller: John Bromley
Height: 11", 27.9 cm
Colour: Cream lustre gown; red cloak trimmed with gold and ermine
Issued: 1996 in a limited edition of 250
Series: Empress

Name	U.S. $	Can. $	U.K. £
Catherine The Great of Russia	1,000.00	1,495.00	495.00

Cathy
Style One

Designer: John Bromley
Modeller: John Bromley
Height: 5", 12.7 cm
Colour: Pink dress, pale green scarf; white hat
Issued: 1986 - 1990
Varieties: Also called Shelley; Vicki
Series: Debutante Collection

Name	U.S. $	Can. $	U.K. £
Cathy (Style One)	130.00	150.00	75.00

Cathy
Style Two

Designer: Val Littlewood
Modeller: Jack Glynn
Height: 10 ¼", 26.5 cm
Colour: Rose-pink
Issued: 1997 in a limited edition of 250
Series: Literary Heroines

Name	U.S. $	Can. $	U.K. £
Cathy (Style Two)	340.00	400.00	195.00

Note: Commissioned by John Sinclair, Sheffield.

Catriona

Designer:	John Bromley
Modeller:	John Bromley
Height:	5 ¼", 13.3 cm
Colour:	Pale yellow dress and hat
Issued:	1987 - 1992
Varieties:	Also called Carla; Penny
Series:	Debutante Collection

Name	U.S. $	Can. $	U.K. £
Catriona	130.00	150.00	75.00

Cavalier

Designer:	Unknown
Height:	8 ¼", 21.0 cm
Colour:	Burgundy, brown and white
Issued:	1979 - unknown

Name	U.S. $	Can. $	U.K. £
Cavalier	395.00	450.00	225.00

Celebration Time

Designer:	Helen Buckley
Modeller:	John Bromley
Height:	5", 12.7 cm
Colour:	Pink
Issued:	1990 to the present
Series:	Debutante Collection

Name	U.S. $	Can. $	U.K. £
Celebration Time	100.00	160.00	52.50

Celeste

Designer:	John Bromley
Modeller:	John Bromley
Height:	6 ½", 16.5 cm
Colour:	Pale blue dress with darker blue flowers
Issued:	1975 - 1979
Varieties:	Also called Angelique; Joy
Series:	Ladies of Fashion

Name	U.S. $	Can. $	U.K. £
Celeste	285.00	325.00	165.00

Celia

Designer:	John Bromley
Height:	8", 20.3 cm
Colour:	White dress with gold highlights; white cat
Issued:	1991 - 1992
Varieties:	Also called Miss 1929
Series:	Roaring Twenties (Style One)

Name	U.S. $	Can. $	U.K. £
Celia	250.00	325.00	165.00

Champagne Reception

Designer:	Elizabeth Greenshields
Modeller:	Jack Glynn
Height:	9 ½", 24.0 cm
Colour:	White and pale yellow
Issued:	1993 - 1993
Series:	Bride of the Year

Name	U.S. $	Can. $	U.K. £
Champagne Reception	350.00	400.00	200.00

Charlotte
Style One

Designer: John Bromley
Modeller: John Bromley
Height: 8 ½", 21.6 cm
Colour: Maroon
Issued: 1976 - 1982
Varieties: Also called Michele; Patricia (Style One)
Series: Ladies of Fashion

Name	**U.S. $**	**Can. $**	**U.K. £**
Charlotte (Style One)	300.00	350.00	175.00

Photograph not available at press time

Charlotte
Style Two

Designer: John Bromley
Height: 9", 22.9 cm
Clothing: Unknown
Issued: 1987 - 1988
Series: Somerset Collection

Name	**U.S. $**	**Can. $**	**U.K. £**
Charlotte (Style Two)	280.00	325.00	160.00

Note: Charlotte is a porcelain figurine dressed in hand-sewn clothing. Prices are for figurine in mint condition with original clothing.

Charlotte
Style Three

Designer: Elizabeth Greenshields
Modeller: Brian Diment
Height: 5 ¾", 14.6 cm
Colour: Pink and pale blue (porcelain)
Issued: 1992 to the present
Series: Beau Monde

Name	**U.S. $**	**Can. $**	**U.K. £**
Charlotte (Style Three)	100.00	235.00	57.50

Charlotte a Royal Debut

Designer:	Shirley Curzon
Modeller:	John Bromley
Height:	8 ¼", 21.0 cm
Colour:	White gown with gold details; pink rose bouquet
Issued:	1990 in a limited edition of 12,500
Series:	Golden Age

Name	U.S. $	Can. $	U.K. £
Charlotte a Royal Debut	225.00	260.00	129.50

Note: Commissioned by Compton and Woodhouse.

Charm

Designer:	Elizabeth Greenshields
Modeller:	John Bromley
Height:	7 ¼", 18.4 cm
Colour:	White and orange
Issued:	1991 - 1993
Varieties:	Also called Finesse
Series:	Chantilly Lace

Name	U.S. $	Can. $	U.K. £
Charm	325.00	375.00	185.00

Cheering the Crew

Designer:	David Shilling
Modeller:	John Bromley
Height:	8 ½", 21.6 cm
Colour:	Mauve and white
Issued:	1989 in a limited edition of 1,000
Series:	Romance of Henley

Name	U.S. $	Can. $	U.K. £
Cheering the Crew	365.00	500.00	245.00

Chelsea

Designer: Elizabeth Greenshields
Modeller: Unknown
Height: 5 ¼", 13.3 cm
Colour: Orange and yellow
Issued: 1993 - 1995
Series: Debutante Collection

Name	U.S. $	Can. $	U.K. £
Chelsea	130.00	150.00	65.00

Chelsea Pensioner

Designer: Margaret Whittaker
Height: 6 ½", 16.5 cm
Colour: Red and black
Issued: 1980 - 1985
Series: London Heritage

Name	U.S. $	Can. $	U.K. £
Chelsea Pensioner	300.00	350.00	175.00

Chelsea Reception

Designer: Helen Buckley
Modeller: David Lyttleton
Height: 6 ¼", 15.9 cm
Colour: Pale blue and lavender (porcelain)
Issued: 1996 to the present
Varieties: Also called Pontefract Princess
Series: Age of Elegance

Name	U.S. $	Can. $	U.K. £
Chelsea Reception	220.00	325.00	110.00

Cherry Seller (The)

Designer:	John Bromley
Height:	8 ¾", 22.2 cm
Colour:	Deep cherry red overdress with white sleeves; peach underskirt; basket of cherries
Issued:	1995 in a limited edition of 9,500
Series:	Cries of London

Name	U.S. $	Can. $	U.K. £
Cherry Seller (The)	280.00	325.00	160.00

Note: Commissioned by Compton and Woodhouse.

Cheryl

Designer:	John Bromley
Modeller:	John Bromley
Height:	7 ¾", 19.7 cm
Colour:	Pale blue
Issued:	1984 - 1986
Varieties:	Also called Victoria (Style Two)
Series:	Ladies of Fashion

Name	U.S. $	Can. $	U.K. £
Cheryl	285.00	325.00	165.00

Cheyne Walk

Designer:	Elizabeth Greenshields
Modeller:	Brian Diment
Height:	8", 20.3 cm
Colour:	Blue and yellow (porcelain)
Issued:	1991 - 1993
Series:	Age of Elegance

Name	U.S. $	Can. $	U.K. £
Cheyne Walk	250.00	325.00	165.00

Chic

Designer:	Elizabeth Greenshields
Modeller:	John Bromley
Height:	7 ¼", 18.4 cm
Colour:	Light blue
Issued:	1991 - 1992
Varieties:	Also called Romance (Style Two); Silk
Series:	Chantilly Lace

Name	U.S. $	Can. $	U.K. £
Chic	285.00	325.00	160.00

Childhood Days

Designer:	Pauline Shone
Height:	5", 12.7 cm
Colour:	Lilac and purple
Issued:	1979 - unknown
Series:	Children Studies

Name	U.S. $	Can. $	U.K. £
Childhood	265.00	300.00	150.00

Childhood Joys

Designer:	Sheila Mitchell
Height:	7 ¼", 18.4 cm
Colour:	Pale blue dress, dark blue bow; pink sash and flowers; light brown hair; straw hat
Issued:	1989 in a limited edition of 12,500
Series:	National Childrens Home

Name	U.S. $	Can. $	U.K. £
Childhood Joys	210.00	240.00	120.00

Note: Commissioned by Compton and Woodhouse and issued to commemorate 120 years of the National Childrens Home.

Chiswick Walk

Designer: Helen Buckley
Modeller: David Lyttleton
Height: 8 ¼", 21.0 cm
Colour: Pale yellow with purple trim (porcelain)
Issued: 1996 to the present
Series: Age of Elegance

Name	U.S. $	Can. $	U.K. £
Chiswick Walk	225.00	395.00	130.00

Chloe
Style One

Designer: John Bromley
Modeller: John Bromley
Height: 3 ¼", 8.3 cm
Colour: Red dress with pink underskirt
Issued: 1985 - 1988
Varieties: Also called Dawn (Style One)
Series: Kensington Collection

Name	U.S. $	Can. $	U.K. £
Chloe (Style One)	85.00	100.00	50.00

Chloe
Style Two

Designer: Elizabeth Greenshields
Modeller: John Bromley
Height: 7 ¼", 18.4 cm
Colour: Lavender and purple
Issued: 1993 - 1993
Varieties: Also called Attraction; Demure; Julia (Style Two)
Series: Chantilly Lace

Name	U.S. $	Can. $	U.K. £
Chloe (Style Two)	300.00	350.00	175.00

Chloe
Style Three

Designer: Unknown
Modeller: Martin Evans
Height: 3 ¾", 9.5 cm
Colour: Mauve
Issued: 1996 to the present
Series: Minuettes

Name	U.S. $	Can. $	U.K. £
Chloe (Style Three)	50.00	105.00	30.00

Christabel
Style One

Designer: John Bromley
Modeller: John Bromley
Height: 8 ½", 21.6 cm
Colour: Gold
Issued: 1976 - 1982
Varieties: Also called Kate (Style One); Rachel (Style One)
Series: Ladies of Fashion

Name	U.S. $	Can. $	U.K. £
Christabel (Style One)	300.00	350.00	175.00

Christabel
Style Two

Designer: John Bromley
Height: 8", 20.3 cm
Colour: Unknown
Issued: 1985
Series: Ladies of Fashion

Name	U.S. $	Can. $	U.K. £
Christabel (Style Two)	250.00	300.00	150.00

Photograph not available at press time

Note: Commissioned by Grattan Home Shopping.

Christina

Designer: John Bromley
Modeller: John Bromley
Height: 7 ¾", 19.7 cm
Colour: 1. Dark blue and green; brown basket containing pink flowers
2. Pale blue dress; brown basket containing pink flowers
Issued: 1977 - 1989
Varieties: Also called Flora (Style One); Summer Breeze (Style One)
Series: Ladies of Fashion

Name	U.S. $	Can. $	U.K. £
1. Dark blue dress	285.00	325.00	165.00
2. Pale blue dress	285.00	325.00	165.00

Christine
Style One

Designer: John Bromley
Height: 7 ¼", 18.5 cm
Colour: Dark blue dress with white frills
Issued: 1975 - 1977
Varieties: Also called Monique; Petite
Series: Ladies of Fashion

Name	U.S. $	Can. $	U.K. £
Christine (Style One)	325.00	375.00	185.00

Christine
Style Two

Designer: John Bromley
Modeller: John Bromley
Height: 5", 12.7 cm
Colour: Lilac
Issued: 1984 - 1988
Varieties: Also called Elaine (Style One); Jacqueline (Style One)
Series: Debutante Collection

Name	U.S. $	Can. $	U.K. £
Christine (Style Two)	165.00	190.00	95.00

Christine
Style Three

Designer: Unknown
Modeller: Jack Glynn
Height: 5 ¾", 14.6 cm
Colour: Lavender (porcelain)
Issued: 1994 to the present
Series: Beau Monde

Name	U.S. $	Can. $	U.K. £
Christine (Style Three)	100.00	150.00	57.50

Photograph not available at press time

Christmas Angel

Designer: Unknown
Modeller: John Bromley
Height: Unknown
Colour: Unknown
Issued: 1985 in a limited edition of 1,500
Series: Christmas Collection

Name	U.S. $	Can. $	U.K. £
Christmas Angel	265.00	300.00	150.00

Christmas Caroller

Designer: Unknown
Modeller: John Bromley
Height: 8", 20.3 cm
Colour: Red and brown
Issued: 1987 in a limited edition of 1,500
Series: Christmas Collection

Name	U.S. $	Can. $	U.K. £
Christmas Caroller	265.00	300.00	150.00

Photograph not available at press time

Christmas Glee

Designer: Unknown
Modeller: John Bromley
Height: Unknown
Colour: Unknown
Issued: 1986 in a limited edition of 1,500
Series: Christmas Collection

Name	U.S. $	Can. $	U.K. £
Christmas Glee	265.00	300.00	150.00

Christmas Kitten (A)

Designer: David Lyttleton
Height: 7 ¼", 18.4 cm
Colour: Peach dress with darker peach flowers and ribbon; tabby kitten in straw basket
Issued: 1993 in a limited edition of 5,000
Series: Barnardo's

Name	U.S. $	Can. $	U.K. £
Christmas Kitten (A)	160.00	180.00	90.00

Note: Commissioned by Compton and Woodhouse.

Cinderella's Ball

Designer: Helen Buckley
Modeller: John Bromley
Height: 4 ¾", 12.1 cm
Colour: Green and blue lustre
Issued: 1996 - 1996
Series: Debutante of the Year

Name	U.S. $	Can. $	U.K. £
Cinderella's Ball	120.00	160.00	95.00

Claire
Style One

Designer:	John Bromley
Modeller:	John Bromley
Height:	5", 12.7 cm
Colour:	Yellow
Issued:	1983 - 1985
Varieties:	Also called Andrea; Maxine; Pamela (Style One); Susan (Style One)
Series:	Debutante Collection

Name	U.S. $	Can. $	U.K. £
Claire (Style One)	165.00	190.00	95.00

Claire
Style Two

Designer:	Helen Buckley
Modeller:	Jack Glynn
Height:	7 ¾", 19.7 cm
Colour:	Pale blue
Issued:	1994 - 1994
Series:	Collingwood Collection (Membership exclusive)

Name	U.S. $	Can. $	U.K. £
Claire (Style Two)	500.00	750.00	250.00

Clara

Designer:	Martin Evans
Height:	4", 10.1 cm
Colour:	Pale green and white (porcelain)
Issued:	1996 - 1997
Series:	Beau Monde

Name	U.S. $	Can. $	U.K. £
Clara	100.00	150.00	57.50

Clare

Designer:	John Bromley
Modeller:	John Bromley
Height:	7 ¾", 19.7 cm
Colour:	Pale blue
Issued:	1975 - 1977
Varieties:	Also called Denise; Sue
Series:	Ladies of Fashion

Name	U.S. $	Can. $	U.K. £
Clare	300.00	350.00	175.00

Clare Marie

Designer:	Helen Buckley
Modeller:	John Bromley
Height:	7 ¾", 19.7 cm
Colour:	Yellow
Issued:	1990 - 1993
Series:	Ladies of Fashion

Name	U.S. $	Can. $	U.K. £
Clare Marie	285.00	325.00	165.00

Clarissa
Style Two

Designer:	Elizabeth Greenshields
Modeller:	Brian Diment
Height:	5 ¼", 13.3 cm
Colour:	Peach and blue (porcelain)
Issued:	1992 - 1994
Series:	Beau Monde

Name	U.S. $	Can. $	U.K. £
Clarissa (Style Two)	150.00	220.00	75.00

Claudette
Style One

Designer: Unknown
Height: Unknown
Colour: Unknown
Issued: 1982 - 1983
Series: Little Women

Name	U.S. $	Can. $	U.K. £
Claudette	165.00	190.00	95.00

Photograph not available at press time

Claudette
Style Two

Designer: John Bromley
Modeller: John Bromley
Height: 5", 12.5 cm
Colour: Green
Issued: 1982 - 1985
Varieties: Also called Annette (Style Four); Jeanette (Style Two); Joanne (Style One); Juliette (Style Two); Lynette (Style Two); Sally Anne (Style One)
Series: Debutante Collection

Name	U.S. $	Can. $	U.K. £
Claudette (Style Two)	165.00	190.00	95.00

Clementine Debut in Paris

Designer: John Bromley
Height: 8 ¼", 21.0 cm
Colour: Pale green dress with gold straps and trimming; pink shawl
Issued: 1991 in a limited edition of 12,500
Series: La Belle Epoque

Name	U.S. $	Can. $	U.K. £
Clementine Debut in Paris	265.00	300.00	150.00

Note: Commissioned by Compton and Woodhouse.

Cleopatra

Designer:	David Cornell
Height:	9 ¼", 23.5 cm
Colour:	White, gold, red and blue
Issued:	1993 in a limited edition of 9,500
Series:	Fabled Beauties

Name	U.S. $	Can. $	U.K. £
Cleopatra	300.00	350.00	175.00

Note: Commissioned by Compton and Woodhouse.

Cobbler (The)

Designer:	Margaret Whittaker
Height:	Unknown
Colour:	Green
Issued:	1974 in a limited edition of 1,000
Series:	Craft Figures

Name	U.S. $	Can. $	U.K.£
Cobbler (The)	300.00	350.00	175.00

Colleen

Designer:	John Bromley
Modeller:	John Bromley
Height:	8 ¼", 21.0 cm
Colour:	Pink dress and hat; rose-pink cape
Issued:	1987 - 1991
Varieties:	Also called Winters Morn
Series:	Ladies of Fashion

Name	U.S. $	Can. $	U.K. £
Colleen	280.00	325.00	160.00

Collette

Designer:	John Bromley
Modeller:	John Bromley
Height:	7 ½", 19.1 cm
Colour:	Blue dress with yellow and white sleeves; yellow and white underskirt
Issued:	1975 - 1982
Varieties:	Also called Blanche (Style One); Rosemary (Style One)
Series:	Ladies of Fashion

Name	U.S. $	Can. $	U.K. £
Collette	300.00	350.00	175.00

Command Performance

Designer:	Elizabeth Greenshields
Modeller:	Brian Diment
Height:	8 ½", 21.6 cm
Colour:	Peach and lavender (porcelain)
Issued:	1991 - 1994
Series:	Age of Elegance

Name	U.S. $	Can. $	U.K. £
Command Performance	285.00	325.00	165.00

Congratulations

Designer:	John Bromley
Modeller:	Unknown
Height:	5", 12.7 cm
Colour:	Green and yellow
Issued:	1992 to the present
Series:	Debutante Collection

Name	U.S. $	Can. $	U.K. £
Congratulations	100.00	150.00	52.50

Constance

Designer:	John Bromley
Modeller:	John Bromley
Height:	7 ½", 19.1 cm
Colour:	Yellow
Issued:	1977 - 1982
Varieties:	Also called Helen (Style One)
Series:	Ladies of Fashion

Name	U.S. $	Can. $	U.K. £
Constance	340.00	400.00	195.00

Cordelia

Designer:	Elizabeth Greenshields
Modeller:	Brian Diment
Height:	5 ¼", 13.3 cm
Colour:	Peach and yellow (porcelain)
Issued:	1992 - 1993
Series:	Beau Monde

Name	U.S. $	Can. $	U.K. £
Cordelia	165.00	190.00	95.00

Corporal, Royal Horse Artillery 1815

Designer:	Unknown
Height:	8 ½", 21.6 cm
Colour:	Dark blue and gold tunic; light blue and brown trousers (porcelain)
Issued:	1990 in a limited edition of 1,000
Series:	Battle of Waterloo Collection

Name	U.S. $	Can. $	U.K. £
Corporal, Royal Horse Artillery 1815	425.00	500.00	250.00

Covent Garden

Designer: Elizabeth Greenshields
Modeller: Brian Diment
Height: 7 ¼", 18.4 cm
Colour: Blue and mauve (porcelain)
Issued: 1992 - 1996
Series: Age of Elegance

Name	U.S. $	Can. $	U.K. £
Covent Garden	285.00	425.00	165.00

Crimean Nurse

Designer: John Bromley
Height: 8 ¼", 21.0 cm
Colour: Pale blue and white
Issued: 1982 in a limited edition of 1,500
Series: Nurses

Name	U.S. $	Can. $	U.K. £
Crimean Nurse	300.00	350.00	175.00

Note: Commissioned by St. Marys Hospital, London to commemorate the Diamond Jubilee of the Nurses League, 1922-1982.

Croquet Game (The)
(circa 1860 - 1863)

Designer: Mary Roberts
Modeller: John Bromley
Height: 7 ½", 19.1 cm
Colour: Blue
Issued: 1985 in a limited edition of 500
Series: Early Days

Name	U.S. $	Can. $	U.K. £
Croquet Game (The)	425.00	500.00	250.00

Note: Commissioned for the Australian market.

Crown (The)

Designer: John Bromley
Height: 5 ½", 14.0 cm
Colour: Brown and green
Issued: 1986 - 1987
Varieties: Also called The Green
Series: The Sporting Collection

Name	U.S. $	Can. $	U.K. £
Crown (The)	385.00	440.00	220.00

Crystal

Designer: John Bromley
Modeller: John Bromley
Height: 8", 20.3 cm
Colour: Brown and cream
Issued: 1984 - 1988
Varieties: Also called Fay
Series: Ladies of Fashion

Name	U.S. $	Can. $	U.K. £
Crystal	300.00	350.00	175.00

Curtain Call

Designer: David Lyttleton
Height: 7 ½", 19.1 cm
Colour: White
Issued: 1993 in a limited edition of 9,500
Series: The Ballet Shoes Collection

Name	U.S. $	Can. $	U.K. £
Curtain Call	160.00	180.00	90.00

Note: Commissioned by Compton and Woodhouse.

Daisy
Style Two

Designer: Jack Glynn
Height: 3 ½", 8.9 cm
Colour: Green overdress; white underskirt with yellow flowers
Issued: 1993 in a limited edition of 15,000
Series: Fairest Flowers

Name	U.S. $	Can. $	U.K. £
Daisy (Style Two)	125.00	140.00	70.00

Note: Commissioned by Compton and Woodhouse.

Photograph not available at press time

Dame Alicia Markova

Designer: John Bromley
Height: 9 ½", 24.0 cm
Colour: White dress with gold flowers; green and white base
Issued: 1995 in a limited edition of 5,000
Series: The Royal Academy of Dancing

Name	U.S. $	Can. $	U.K. £
Dame Alicia Markova	315.00	360.00	180.00

Note: Commissioned by Compton and Woodhouse.

Dame Antoinette Sibley

Designer: John Bromley
Height: 10 ½", 26.7 cm
Colour: Pale pink dress with red flowers, gold trim around flowers; pink and white base
Issued: 1996 in a limited edition of 5,000
Series: The Royal Academy of Dancing

Name	U.S. $	Can. $	U.K. £
Dame Antoinette Sibley	315.00	360.00	180.00

Note: Commissioned by Compton and Woodhouse.

Dame Margot Fonteyn

Designer:	John Bromley
Height:	11", 27.9 cm
Colour:	White dress with gold details
Issued:	1994 in a limited edition of 5,000
Series:	The Royal Academy of Dancing

Name	U.S. $	Can. $	U.K. £
Dame Margot Fonteyn	315.00	360.00	180.00

Note: Commissioned by Compton and Woodhouse.

Dance of Dawn

Designer:	John Bromley
Modeller:	John Bromley
Height:	8 ¾", 22.2 cm
Colour:	Pale blue
Issued:	1976 - 1982
Series:	Ladies of Fashion

Name	U.S. $	Can. $	U.K. £
Dance of Dawn	300.00	350.00	175.00

Photograph not available at press time

Danielle
Style One

Designer:	Unknown
Height:	Unknown
Colour:	Unknown
Issued:	1982 - 1983
Series:	Little Women

Name	U.S. $	Can. $	U.K. £
Danielle (Style One)	165.00	190.00	95.00

Danielle
Style Two

Designer:	John Bromley
Modeller:	John Bromley
Height:	5", 12.7 cm
Colour:	White dress with green trim
Issued:	1982 - 1985
Varieties:	Also called Giselle (Style Two); June (Style Three); Karen (Style One); Michelle (Style Two)
Series:	Debutante Collection

Name	U.S. $	Can. $	U.K. £
Danielle (Style Two)	165.00	190.00	95.00

Danielle
Style Three

Designer:	Unknown
Modeller:	Martin Evans
Height:	3 ½", 8.9 cm
Colour:	Lemon and blue
Issued:	1995 - 1997
Varieties:	Also called Jessica (Style Two)
Series:	Minuettes

Name	U.S. $	Can. $	U.K. £
Danielle (Style Three)	50.00	79.50	30.00

Daphne
Style One

Designer:	Helen Buckley
Modeller:	John Bromley
Height:	8", 20.3 cm
Colour:	Red and pink
Issued:	1986 - 1993
Series:	Ladies of Fashion

Name	U.S. $	Can. $	U.K. £
Daphne (Style One)	250.00	290.00	145.00

Photograph not available at press time

Daphne
Style Two

Designer:	Jack Glynn
Height:	3 ½", 8.9 cm
Colour:	Deep pink overdress; pale pink underskirt with yellow flowers
Issued:	1993 in a limited edition of 15,000
Series:	Fairest Flowers

Name	U.S. $	Can. $	U.K. £
Daphne (Style Two)	125.00	140.00	69.00

Note: Commissioned by Compton and Woodhouse.

Davina

Designer:	John Bromley
Modeller:	John Bromley
Height:	7 ½", 19.1 cm
Colour:	Burgundy and grey
Issued:	1985
Varieties:	Also called Janet; Moira
Series:	Ladies of Fashion

Name	U.S. $	Can. $	U.K. £
Davina	280.00	325.00	160.00

Note: Commissioned by Grattan Home Shopping.

Dawn
Style One

Designer:	John Bromley
Modeller:	John Bromley
Height:	3 ¼", 8.3 cm
Colour:	Yellow dress with pale yellow underskirt
Issued:	1985 - 1988
Varieties:	Also called Chloe (Style One)
Series:	Kensington Collection

Name	U.S. $	Can. $	U.K. £
Dawn (Style One)	85.00	100.00	50.00

Dawn
Style Two

Designer: Helen Buckley
Modeller: Andy Moss
Height: 5", 12.7 cm
Colour: Rose-pink
Issued: 1997 to the present
Series: Debutante Collection

Name	U.S. $	Can. $	U.K. £
Dawn (Style Two)	100.00	155.00	52.50

Debbie

Designer: John Bromley
Modeller: John Bromley
Height: 8", 20.3 cm
Colour: Pale blue
Issued: 1977 - 1989
Varieties: Also called Gillian (Style One); Linda (Style One); Melody; Philippa (Style One)
Series: Ladies of Fashion

Name	U.S. $	Can. $	U.K. £
Debbie	250.00	290.00	145.00

Deborah

Designer: Elizabeth Greenshields
Modeller: Martin Evans
Height: 5 ¼", 13.3 cm
Colour: Pale blue and pink (porcelain)
Issued: 1993 - 1994
Series: Beau Monde

Name	U.S. $	Can. $	U.K. £
Deborah	165.00	235.00	95.00

Dee

Designer: John Bromley
Modeller: John Bromley
Height: 5", 12.7 cm
Colour: Royal blue
Issued: 1986 - 1989
Varieties: Also called Lindsay; Zara
Series: Debutante Collection

Name	U.S. $	Can. $	U.K. £
Dee	160.00	180.00	90.00

Delilah
(on wooden plinth)

Designer: David Cornell
Height: 10", 25.4 cm
Colour: Pale green and lilac dress with dark green peacock feathers; gold trimmings
Issued: 1996 in a limited edition of 9,500
Series: Fabled Beauties

Name	U.S. $	Can. $	U.K. £
Delilah	300.00	350.00	175.00

Note: Commissioned by Compton and Woodhouse.

Demetria

Designer: Helen Buckley
Modeller: John Bromley
Height: 7 ¾", 19.7 cm
Colour: Lavender and purple
Issued: 1986 - 1996
Series: Ladies of Fashion

Name	U.S. $	Can. $	U.K. £
Demetria	275.00	325.00	165.00

Demure

Designer:	Elizabeth Greenshields
Modeller:	John Bromley
Height:	7 ¼", 18.4 cm
Colour:	Pale pink
Issued:	1991 - 1992
Varieties:	Also called Attraction; Chloe (Style Two); Julia (Style Two)
Series:	Chantilly Lace

Name	U.S. $	Can. $	U.K. £
Demure	300.00	350.00	175.00

Denise

Designer:	John Bromley
Modeller:	John Bromley
Height:	7 ¾", 19.5 cm
Colour:	Pink bodice; white skirt with yellow and red flowers
Issued:	1975 - 1977
Varieties:	Also called Clare; Sue
Series:	Ladies of Fashion

Name	U.S. $	Can. $	U.K. £
Denise	325.00	375.00	185.00

Devotion

Designer:	John Bromley
Height:	7 ¼", 18.4 cm
Colour:	Mother in pink dress; daughter in white dress
Issued:	1980 - 1982
Series:	Ladies of Fashion

Name	U.S. $	Can. $	U.K. £
Devotion	395.00	450.00	225.00

Diana

Designer:	Unknown
Height:	7 ¾", 19.7 cm
Colour:	Purple and lilac
Issued:	1993 to the present
Series:	Ladies of Fashion

Name	U.S. $	Can. $	U.K. £
Diana	225.00	325.00	110.00

Diane

Designer:	John Bromley
Height:	Unknown
Colour:	Unknown
Issued:	1984
Series:	Ladies of Fashion

Name	U.S. $	Can. $	U.K. £
Diane	250.00	290.00	145.00

Note: Commissioned By Grattan Home Shopping.

Photograph not available at press time

Dianne

Designer:	John Bromley
Modeller:	John Bromley
Height:	7 ½", 19.1 cm
Colour:	Flowered jade dress
Issued:	1975 - 1977
Varieties:	Also called Anne (Style One); Sophia (Style One)
Series:	Ladies of Fashion

Name	U.S. $	Can. $	U.K. £
Dianne	300.00	350.00	175.00

Dick Turpin

Designer:	Unknown
Height:	Unknown
Colour:	Unknown
Issued:	1986 - 1987
Series:	Romance and Legend

Name	U.S. $	Can. $	U.K. £
Dick Turpin	475.00	550.00	275.00

Photograph not available at press time

Dignity

Designer:	John Bromley
Modeller:	John Bromley
Height:	7 ¼", 18.4 cm
Colour:	Purple and blue
Issued:	1991 - 1992
Varieties:	Also called High Style; Lace
Series:	Chantilly Lace

Name	U.S. $	Can. $	U.K. £
Dignity	285.00	325.00	165.00

Dinner at 8

Designer:	David Shilling
Modeller:	John Bromley
Height:	8 ¾", 22.2 cm
Colour:	Pink and light green
Issued:	1987 in a limited edition of 1,000
Series:	Designer Series

Name	U.S. $	Can. $	U.K. £
Dinner at 8	475.00	550.00	275.00

Photograph not available at press time

District Nurse

Designer:	John Bromley
Height:	Unknown
Colour:	Unknown
Issued:	1983
Series:	Nurses

Name	U.S. $	Can. $	U.K. £
District Nurse	265.00	300.00	150.00

Donna
Style One

Designer:	John Bromley
Modeller:	John Bromley
Height:	8", 20.3 cm
Colour:	Pale blue
Issued:	1980 - 1988
Series:	Ladies of Fashion

Name	U.S. $	Can. $	U.K. £
Donna (Style One)	285.00	325.00	165.00

Donna
Style Two

Designer:	Helen Buckley
Modeller:	John Bromley
Height:	8 ½", 21.6 cm
Colour:	Blue and white (porcelain)
Issued:	1997
Varieties:	Also called Cafe Royal
Series:	Age of Elegance

Name	U.S. $	Can. $	U..K. £
Donna (Style Two)	160.00	180.00	88.99

Note: Commissioned by Empire Stores Home Shopping.

Photograph not available at press time

Dorothy
Style One

Designer: John Bromley
Height: 8", 20.3 cm
Colour: Unknown
Issued: 1986
Series: Ladies of Fashion

Name	U.S. $	Can. $	U.K. £
Dorothy (Style One)	265.00	300.00	150.00

Note: Commissioned by Kays, England.

Photograph not available at press time

Dorothy
Style Two

Designer: John Bromley
Height: 8", 20.3 cm
Colour: Unknown
Issued: 1987
Series: Ladies of Fashion

Name	U.S. $	Can. $	U.K. £
Dorothy (Style Two)	265.00	300.00	150.00

Note: Sold exclusively through the Seven Seas Giftshop, Mount Bridges, Canada. Original issue price $175.00.

Dorothy
Style Three

Designer: Helen Buckley
Modeller: Jack Glynn
Height: 8", 20.3 cm
Colour: Rose-pink
Issued: 1997 to the present
Series: Ladies of Fashion

Name	U.S. $	Can. $	U.K. £
Dorothy (Style Three)	195.00	330.00	110.00

Duke of Wellington

Designer: Robert Worthington
Height: 9", 22.9 cm
Colour: Dark blue-green jacket and cloak; yellow breeches; black hat and boots
Issued: Unknown

Name	U.S. $	Can. $	U.K. £
Duke of Wellington	395.00	450.00	225.00

Dulcie

Designer: John Bromley
Modeller: John Bromley
Height: 7 ¾", 19.7 cm
Colour: Dark blue
Issued: 1986 - 1988
Series: Ladies of Fashion

Name	U.S. $	Can. $	U.K. £
Dulcie	285.00	325.00	165.00

Earth

Designer: Sue Cashmore
Modeller: John Bromley
Height: 10 ¾", 27.8 cm
Colour: Green and white
Issued: 1989 in a limited edition of 1,000
Series: The Elements

Name	U.S. $	Can. $	U.K. £
Earth	400.00	475.00	235.00

Easter Bonnet

Designer: Elizabeth Greenshields
Modeller: Brian Diment
Height: 8 ¼", 21.0 cm
Colour: Peach and pale blue (porcelain)
Issued: 1993 - 1996
Series: Age of Elegance

Name	U.S. $	Can. $	U.K. £
Easter Bonnet	285.00	465.00	165.00

Edith Cavell

Designer: John Bromley
Height: 8 ½", 21.6 cm
Colour: Blue, grey and black
Issued: 1981 in a limited edition of 500

Name	U.S. $	Can. $	U.K. £
Edith Cavell	340.00	400.00	195.00

Edwina

Designer: John Bromley
Height: Unknown
Colour: Unknown
Issued: 1987 - 1988
Series: Edwardian Beauties

Name	U.S. $	Can. $	U.K. £
Edwina	285.00	325.00	165.00

Photograph not available at press time

Eileen

Designer:	John Bromley
Modeller:	John Bromley
Height:	8 ¼", 21.0 cm
Colour:	Lilac
Issued:	1978 - 1984
Varieties:	Also called Emma (Style One); Frances; The Hostess; Victoria (Style One)
Series:	Ladies of Fashion

Name	U.S. $	Can. $	U.K. £
Eileen	285.00	325.00	165.00

Elaine
Style One

Designer:	John Bromley
Modeller:	John Bromley
Height:	5", 12.7 cm
Colour:	Blue
Issued:	1984 - 1988
Varieties:	Also called Christine (Style Two); Jacqueline (Style One)
Series:	Debutante Collection

Name	U.S. $	Can. $	U.K. £
Elaine (Style One)	165.00	190.00	95.00

Elaine
Style Two

Designer:	Elizabeth Greenshields
Modeller:	Jack Glynn
Height:	8 ½", 21.6 cm
Colour:	Green and pink (porcelain)
Issued:	1997
Varieties:	Also called "Name Your Own"; Summer Breeze (Style Two)
Series:	Ladies of Fashion

Name	U.S. $	Can. $	U.K. £
Elaine (Style Two)	175.00	200.00	99.95

Note: Commissioned by Wellington Gifts, Ballymena, Northern Ireland.

Eleanor
Style One

Designer: John Bromley
Modeller: John Bromley
Height: 5 ¼", 13.3 cm
Colour: Red coat; white underskirt
Issued: 1985 - 1988
Varieties: Also called Grace (Style One); Penelope (Style Two)
Series: Debutante Collection

Name	U.S. $	Can. $	U.K. £
Eleanor (Style One)	150.00	170.00	85.00

Eleanor
Style Two

Designer: Graham Miller
Modeller: Graham Miller
Height: 10", 25.4 cm
Colour: Pink
Issued: 1997 to the present
Varieties: Also called Gillian (Style Three)
Series: Silhouettes

Name	U.S. $	Can. $	U.K. £
Eleanor (Style Two)	150.00	235.00	72.50

Elegance

Designer: Helen Buckley
Modeller: John Bromley
Height: 8 ½", 21.6 cm
Colour: Grey-blue dress; mottled green stole
Issued: 1988 - 1994
Series: Ladies of Fashion

Name	U.S. $	Can. $	U.K. £
Elegance	280.00	395.00	160.00

Elegant Fifties (The)

Designer:	John Bromley
Height:	9", 22.9 cm
Colour:	Lady - pale yellow dress Gentleman - dark green jacket with gold epaulettes; pale yellow pantaloons; white stockings; black shoes
Issued:	1981 - 1984
Series:	Dancing Years

Name	U.S. $	Can. $	U.K. £
Elegant Fifties (The)	425.00	500.00	245.00

Elegant Eighties (The)

Designer:	John Bromley
Height:	8 ¾", 22.2 cm
Colour:	Pink
Issued:	1982 - 1984
Series:	Dancing Years

Name	U.S. $	Can. $	U.K. £
Elegant Eighties (The)	465.00	525.00	265.00

Photograph not available at press time

Photograph not available at press time

Elena

Designer:	Helen Buckley
Modeller:	John Bromley
Height:	9", 22.9 cm
Clothing	Unknown
Issued:	1987-1988
Series:	Somerset Collection

Name	U.S. $	Can. $	U.K. £
Elena	215.00	250.00	125.00

Note: Elena is a porcelain figurine dressed in hand-sewn clothing. Prices are for figurine in mint condition with original clothing.

Elisa

Designer: John Bromley
Modeller: John Bromley
Height: 3 ¼", 8.3 cm
Colour: Pale pink
Issued: 1985 - 1988
Varieties: Also called Sharon (Style One)
Series: Kensington Collection

Name	U.S. $	Can. $	U.K. £
Elisa	85.00	100.00	50.00

Elizabeth
Style One

Designer: John Bromley
Modeller: John Bromley
Height: 6 ½", 16.5 cm
Colour: Light brown
Issued: 1977 - 1982
Varieties: Also called Lisa (Style One); Polly
Series: Ladies of Fashion

Name	U.S. $	Can. $	U.K. £
Elizabeth (Style One)	340.00	400.00	195.00

Elizabeth
Style Two

Designer: Elizabeth Greenshields
Modeller: Martin Evans
Height: 5 ½", 14.0 cm
Colour: Pale lavender and lemon (porcelain)
Issued: 1992 to the present
Series: Beau Monde

Name	U.S. $	Can. $	U.K. £
Elizabeth (Style Two)	100.00	235.00	57.50

Ellen

Designer:	Andy Moss
Modeller:	Andy Moss
Height:	5", 12.7 cm
Colour:	Lavender (porcelain)
Issued:	1997 to the present
Series:	Beau Monde

Name	U.S. $	Can. $	U.K. £
Ellen	100.00	175.00	57.50

Ellen Terry
(1848 - 1928)

Designer:	John Bromley
Height:	10", 25.4 cm
Colour:	Yellow dress
Issued:	1981 in a limited edition of 500

Name	U.S. $	Can. $	U.K. £
Ellen Terry (1848-1928)	700.00	950.00	475.00

Photograph not available at press time

Eloise

Designer:	John Bromley
Height:	5", 12.7 cm
Colour:	Unknown
Issued:	1986
Series:	Debutante Collection

Name	U.S. $	Can. $	U.K. £
Eloise	175.00	200.00	100.00

Note: Commissioned by Grattan Home Shopping.

Emerald

Designer:	Maureen Halson
Height:	9 ½", 24.0 cm
Colour:	Jade dress; white and blue flowers; gold highlights
Issued:	1992 in a limited edition of 9,500
Series:	Spirits of the Jewels

Name	U.S. $	Can. $	U.K. £
Emerald	280.00	325.00	158.00

Note: Commissioned by Compton and Woodhouse.

Emily

Designer:	John Bromley
Modeller:	John Bromley
Height:	8", 20.3 cm
Colour:	Yellow dress with white underskirt
Issued:	1977 to the present
Varieties:	Also called Alison; Flair; Heather (Style One); Henrietta
Series:	Ladies of Fashion

Name	U.S. $	Can. $	U.K. £
Emily	195.00	345.00	110.00

Emma
Style One

Designer:	John Bromley
Modeller:	John Bromley
Height:	8 ¼", 21.0 cm
Colour:	Pale blue
Issued:	1975 - 1988
Varieties:	Also called Eileen; Frances; The Hostess; Victoria (Style One)
Series:	Ladies of Fashion

Name	U.S. $	Can. $	U.K. £
Emma (Style One)	285.00	325.00	165.00

Emma
Style Two

Designer: Elizabeth Greenshields
Modeller: John Bromley
Height: 8 ¼", 21.0 cm
Colour: Peach and beige
Issued: 1993 - 1993
Series: Special Events

Name	U.S. $	Can. $	U.K. £
Emma (Style Two)	500.00	600.00	295.00

Emma
Style Three

Designer: Unknown
Modeller: Martin Evans
Height: 3 ½", 8.9 cm
Colour: Blue
Issued: 1996 to the present
Series: Minuettes

Name	U.S. $	Can. $	U.K. £
Emma (Style Three)	50.00	105.00	30.00

Emma Hamilton

Designer: Raymond Hughes
Modeller: John Bromley
Height: 8 ¼", 21.0 cm
Colour: Cream dress with blue bows; pale blue shawl; blue hat with pale blue bow; beige muff; gold trim
Issued: 1991 in a limited edition of 12,500
Series: Femmes Fatales

Name	U.S. $	Can. $	U.K. £
Emma Hamilton	280.00	325.00	160.00

Note: Commissioned by Compton and Woodhouse.

Emma Jane

Designer:	Shirley Curzon
Modeller:	Martin Evans
Height:	8", 20.3 cm
Colour:	Rose-pink
Issued:	1997 to the present
Varieties:	Also called Pauline
Series:	Ladies of Fashion

Name	U.S. $	Can. $	U.K. £
Emma Jane	195.00	220.00	109.99

Note: Commissioned by G.U.S. Home Shopping.

Emma Louise

Designer:	John Bromley
Modeller:	John Bromley
Height:	5", 12.7 cm
Colour:	White with gold trim
Issued:	1988 - 1991
Series:	Debutante Collection

Name	U.S. $	Can. $	U.K. £
Emma Louise	150.00	170.00	85.00

Empress Josephine

Designer:	Raymond Hughes
Modeller:	John Bromley
Height:	8 ½", 21.6 cm
Colour:	Cream dress with gold designs; pale pink overskirt with gold trim; gold tiara and fan
Issued:	1993 in a limited edition of 12,500
Series:	Femmes Fatales

Name	U.S. $	Can. $	U.K. £
Empress Josephine	280.00	325.00	158.00

Note: Commissioned by Compton and Woodhouse.

Enchanted Evening

Designer:	Shirley Curzon
Modeller:	Martin Evans
Height:	8", 20.3 cm
Colour:	Lavender and cream
Issued:	1997 in a limited edition of 1,000
Series:	Ladies of Fashion

Name	U.S. $	Can. $	U.K. £
Enchanted Evening	195.00	220.00	110.00

Note: Commissioned by Guild of Specialist China and Glass.

Enchanted Lily

Designer:	Helen Buckley
Modeller:	Jack Glynn
Height:	8", 20.3 cm
Colour:	Unknown
Issued:	1997 in a limited edition of 250
Varieties:	Also called Fairest Lily; Gracious Lily
Series:	Flower Ladies

Name	U.S. $	Can. $	U.K. £
Enchanted Lily	N/A	N/A	N/A

Note: Commissioned for the Australian market, with a retail price of Aust.$595.00.

Enchantress

Designer:	John Bromley
Modeller:	John Bromley
Height:	8 ½", 21.6 cm
Colour:	Lilac dress with purple flowered bodice
Issued:	1984 - 1989
Varieties:	Also called Antonia; Marjorie
Series:	Ladies of Fashion

Name	U.S. $	Can. $	U.K. £
Enchantress	300.00	350.00	175.00

Encore

Designer: John Bromley
Modeller: John Bromley
Height: 5", 12.7 cm
Colour: Lemon dress and hat; blue scarf
Issued: 1989 - 1991
Varieties: Also called Carrie
Series: Debutante Collection

Name	U.S. $	Can. $	U.K. £
Encore	165.00	190.00	95.00

Endless Love

Designer: Unknown
Height: 5", 12.7 cm
Colour: Rose-pink and pale pink
Issued: 1996 - 1996
Varieties: Also called Violet (Style One)
Series: Valentine Debutante of the Year

Name	U.S. $	Can. $	U.K. £
Endless Love	130.00	150.00	75.00

English Elegance

Designer: John Bromley
Modeller: John Bromley
Height: 8 ¾", 22.2 cm
Colour: Pink and white
Issued: 1994 in a limited edition of 1,000
Series: English Rose

Name	U.S. $	Can. $	U.K. £
English Elegance	1,000.00	1,100.00	575.00

Erin

Designer:	Helen Buckley
Modeller:	Jack Glynn
Height:	8", 20.3 cm
Colour:	Blue
Issued:	1997 in a limited edition of 1,200
Series:	The Hampshire Collection

Name	U.S. $	Can. $	U.K. £
Erin	N/A	275.00	N/A

Note: Commissioned exclusively for the Canadian market.

Esplanade

Designer:	Elizabeth Greenshields
Modeller:	Martin Evans
Height:	8 ¼", 21.0 cm
Colour:	Blue and yellow (porcelain)
Issued:	1992 - 1994
Series:	Age of Elegance

Name	U.S. $	Can. $	U.K. £
Esplanade	300.00	350.00	175.00

Photograph not available at press time

Estelle
Style One

Designer:	Unknown
Height:	Unknown
Colour:	Unknown
Issued:	1982 - 1983
Series:	Little Women

Name	U.S. $	Can. $	U.K. £
Estelle (Style One)	165.00	190.00	95.00

Estelle
Style Two

Designer: John Bromley
Modeller: John Bromley
Height: 5", 12.7 cm
Colour: White with gold trim
Issued: 1982 - 1985
Varieties: Also called Jennifer (Style Two); Nanette (Style Two); Nicolette (Style Two); Paulette (Style Two)
Series: Debutante Collection

Name	U.S. $	Can. $	U.K. £
Estelle (Style Two)	165.00	190.00	95.00

Estelle
Style Three

Designer: Elizabeth Greenshields
Modeller: Brian Diment
Height: 5", 12.7 cm
Colour: Blue and yellow (porcelain)
Issued: 1992 - 1994
Series: Beau Monde

Name	U.S. $	Can. $	U.K. £
Estelle (Style Three)	215.00	250.00	80.00

Eternity

Designer: Unknown
Modeller: Martin Evans
Height: 5", 12.7 cm
Colour: Purple
Issued: 1997 - 1997
Varieties: Also called Amy (Style Two)
Series: Valentine Debutante of the Year

Name	U.S. $	Can. $	U.K. £
Eternity	90.00	125.00	50.00

Eugenie

Designer: Helen Buckley
Modeller: John Bromley
Height: 8 ¼", 21.0 cm
Colour: Pink and blue
Issued: 1986 - 1988
Series: Ladies of Fashion

Name	U.S. $	Can. $	U.K. £
Eugenie	285.00	325.00	165.00

Eugenie First Night at the Opera

Designer: Shirley Curzon
Modeller: John Bromley
Height: 8 ¼", 21.0 cm
Colour: Lilac dress with gold highlights
Issued: 1990 in a limited edition of 12,500
Series: Golden Age

Name	U.S. $	Can. $	U.K. £
Eugenie First Night at the Opera	225.00	260.00	130.00

Note: Commissioned by Compton and Woodhouse.

Eve

Designer: Andrea Cox
Modeller: Jack Glynn
Height: 12", 30.5 cm
Colour: Lemon dress; green scarf and headband
Issued: 1997 to the present
Series: The Roaring Twenties (Style Two)

Name	U.S. $	Can. $	U.K. £
Eve	215.00	485.00	125.00

Evening at the Opera

Designer:	John Bromley
Modeller:	John Bromley
Height:	8 ½", 21.6 cm
Colour:	Pink (porcelain)
Issued:	1995 - 1997
Varieties:	Also called Antonia (Style Two)
Series:	Age of Elegance

Name	U.S. $	Can. $	U.K. £
Evening at the Opera	195.00	260.00	110.00

Evening Ball

Designer:	Elizabeth Greenshields
Modeller:	Brian Diment
Height:	10", 25.4 cm
Colour:	Pink and yellow (porcelain)
Issued:	1993 in a limited edition of 2,000
Series:	Turn of the Century

Name	U.S. $	Can. $	U.K. £
Evening Ball	600.00	750.00	350.00

Evening Promenade

Designer:	Elizabeth Greenshields
Modeller:	Jack Glynn
Height:	8 ¾", 22.2 cm
Colour:	Lilac and mauve (porcelain)
Issued:	1995 - 1995
Series:	Age of Elegance Figurine of the Year

Name	U.S. $	Can. $	U.K. £
Evening Promenade	295.00	325.00	175.00

Evening Stroll

Designer:	Val Littlewood
Modeller:	John Bromley
Height:	9", 22.9 cm
Colour:	Blue, green and cream
Issued:	1989 - 1991
Series:	Ladies of Leisure

Name	U.S. $	Can. $	U.K. £
Evening Stroll	300.00	350.00	175.00

Fairest Lily

Designer:	Helen Buckley
Modeller:	Jack Glynn
Height:	8", 20.3 cm
Colour:	Pink and white
Issued:	1996 in a limited edition of 2,000
Varieties:	Also called Enchanted Lily; Gracious Lily
Series:	Flower Ladies

Name	U.S. $	Can. $	U.K. £
Fairest Lily	650.00	895.00	375.00

Photograph not available at press time

Faith

Designer:	John Bromley
Height:	8", 20.3 cm
Colour:	Unknown
Issued:	1986
Series:	Ladies of Fashion

Name	U.S. $	Can. $	U.K. £
Faith	265.00	300.00	150.00

Note: Commissioned by Kays.

Fascination

Designer:	John Bromley
Modeller:	John Bromley
Height:	4", 10.1 cm
Colour:	Green and lilac
Issued:	1991 to the present
Varieties:	Also called In Love
Series:	Debutante Collection

Name	U.S. $	Can. $	U.K. £
Fascination	100.00	160.00	52.50

Fay

Designer:	John Bromley
Modeller:	John Bromley
Height:	8", 20.3 cm
Colour:	Red
Issued:	1984 - 1988
Varieties:	Also called Crystal
Series:	Ladies of Fashion

Name	U.S. $	Can. $	U.K. £
Fay	300.00	350.00	175.00

Feeding Time

Designer:	Pauline Shone
Height:	8 ½", 21.6 cm
Colour:	Cream, white and black
Issued:	1979 - unknown
Series:	Children Studies

Name	U.S. $	Can. $	U.K. £
Feeding Time	250.00	290.00	145.00

Felicity

Designer:	John Bromley
Modeller:	John Bromley
Height:	8 ¼", 21.0 cm
Colour:	Yellow dress with orange highlights
Issued:	1984 - 1987
Varieties:	Also called Alexis
Series:	Ladies of Fashion

Name	U.S. $	Can. $	U.K. £
Felicity	300.00	350.00	175.00

Finesse

Designer:	Elizabeth Greenshields
Modeller:	John Bromley
Height:	7 ¼", 18.4 cm
Colour:	White and yellow dress with gold highlights
Issued:	1991 - 1993
Varieties:	Also called Charm
Series:	Chantilly Lace

Name	U.S. $	Can. $	U.K. £
Finesse	300.00	350.00	175.00

Fiona
Style One

Designer:	John Bromley
Modeller:	John Bromley
Height:	8 ½", 21.6 cm
Colour:	Royal blue and white
Issued:	1975 - 1979
Varieties:	Also called Alice; Georgina (Style One)
Series:	Ladies of Fashion

Name	U.S. $	Can. $	U.K. £
Fiona (Style One)	250.00	290.00	145.00

Fiona
Style Two

Designer:	John Bromley
Height:	5", 12.7 cm
Colour:	Unknown
Issued:	1989
Series:	Debutante Collection

Name	U.S. $	Can. $	U.K. £
Fiona (Style Two)	165.00	190.00	95.00

Note: Commissioned by W. W. Securities.

Photograph not available at press time

Fiona
Style Three

Designer:	Elizabeth Greenshields
Modeller:	Jack Glynn
Height:	5 ½", 14.0 cm
Colour:	Pale blue skirt and jacket with darker blue collar, cuffs and hem
Issued:	1994 - 1997
Series:	Debutante Collection

Name	U.S. $	Can. $	U.K. £
Fiona (Style Three)	100.00	150.00	52.50

Fire

Designer:	Sue Cashmore
Modeller:	John Bromley
Height:	11 ¾", 29.8 cm
Colour:	Rose-pink, pale pink and yellow
Issued:	1989 in a limited edition of 1,000
Series:	The Elements

Name	U.S. $	Can. $	U.K. £
Fire	425.00	500.00	245.00

Fire Fighter (The)

Designer: John Bromley
Height: 7 ¾", 19.5 cm
Colour: Black and orange
Issued: 1985 in a limited edition of 5,000

Name	U.S. $	Can. $	U.K. £
Fire Fighter	285.00	325.00	165.00

Note: Commissioned by the Fire Services.

First Catch
(on wooden plinth)

Designer: John Bromley
Height: 7", 17.8 cm
Colour: Greens and brown
Issued: 1984 - 1987
Series: Sporting Collection

Name	U.S. $	Can. $	U.K. £
First Catch	395.00	450.00	225.00

First Dance

Designer: John Bromley
Modeller: John Bromley
Height: 8", 20.3 cm
Colour: Pink
Issued: 1984 - 1989
Varieties: Also called Loves Dream; Melanie (Style One)
Series: Ladies of Fashion

Name	U.S. $	Can. $	U.K. £
First Dance	285.00	325.00	165.00

First Tee
(on wooden plinth)

Designer: John Bromley
Height: 8", 20.3 cm
Colour: Green-blue and yellow
Issued: 1984 - 1987
Series: Sporting Collection

Name	U.S. $	Can. $	U.K. £
First Tee	395.00	450.00	225.00

First Visit

Designer: David Shilling
Modeller: John Bromley
Height: 8 ½", 21.6 cm
Colour: Yellow
Issued: 1989 in a limited edition of 1,000
Series: Romance of Henley

Name	U.S. $	Can. $	U.K. £
First Visit	395.00	450.00	225.00

First Waltz

Designer: Helen Buckley
Modeller: Jack Glynn
Height: 8 ¼", 21.0 cm
Colour: Lilac and purple (porcelain)
Issued: 1996 - 1996
Series: Age of Elegance Porcelain Figure of the Year

Name	U.S. $	Can. $	U.K. £
First Waltz	265.00	295.00	150.00

Flair

Designer: John Bromley
Modeller: John Bromley
Height: 8", 20.3 cm
Colour: Red dress with yellow underskirt
Issued: 1984 - 1991
Varieties: Also called Alison; Emily; Heather (Style One); Henrietta
Series: Ladies of Fashion

Name	U.S. $	Can. $	U.K. £
Flair	285.00	325.00	165.00

Fleur

Designer: Helen Buckley
Modeller: John Bromley
Height: 7 ¾", 19.7 cm
Colour: White dress with gold highlights
Issued: 1991 - 1993
Varieties: Also called Bolero
Series: Grosvenor Collection

Name	U.S. $	Can. $	U.K. £
Fleur	300.00	350.00	175.00

Flora
Style One

Designer: John Bromley
Modeller: John Bromley
Height: 7 ¾", 19.7 cm
Colour: Peach dress; dark blue or black bow to hat; brown basket
Issued: 1977 - 1989
Varieties: Also called Christina; Summer Breeze (Style One)
Series: Ladies of Fashion

Name	U.S. $	Can. $	U.K. £
Flora (Style One)	280.00	340.00	160.00

Flora
Style Two

Designer: Unknown
Modeller: Jack Glynn
Height: 3 ½", 8.9 cm
Colour: Deep pink bodice; white skirt with pink flowers; gold trim
Issued: 1993 in a limited edition of 15,000
Series: Fairest Flowers

Name	U.S. $	Can. $	U.K. £
Flora (Style Two)	125.00	140.00	70.00

Note: Commissioned by Compton and Woodhouse.

Florence Nightingale

Designer: John Bromley
Height: 8 ½", 21.6 cm
Colour: Rose-pink and white jacket; dark blue skirt
Issued: 1981 - 1982

Name	U.S. $	Can. $	U.K. £
Florence Nightingale	600.00	700.00	350.00

Flower Fairy

Designer: Sheila Mitchell
Modeller: John Bromley
Height: 7 ½", 19.1 cm
Colour: White
Issued: 1992 in a limited edition of 9,500
Series: The Ballet Shoes Collection

Name	U.S. $	Can. $	U.K. £
Flower Fairy	140.00	160.00	80.00

Note: Commissioned by Compton and Woodhouse.

Flower Girl
Style One

Designer: John Bromley
Height: 6", 15.0 cm
Colour: Pink
Issued: 1980 - 1985
Varieties: Also called Bridesmaid (Style Four)
Series: Ladies of Fashion

Name	U.S. $	Can. $	U.K. £
Flower Girl (Style One)	300.00	350.00	175.00

Flower Girl (The)
Style Two

Designer: John Bromley
Height: 7 ¾", 19.7 cm
Colour: Dark green bodice and red skirt; white bird
Issued: 1984 in a limited edition of 1,000
Series: Arcadian Collection

Name	U.S. $	Can. $	U.K. £
Flower Girl (Style Two)	340.00	400.00	195.00

Flower Seller (The)
Style One

Designer: Margaret Whittaker
Height: 7", 17.8 cm
Colour: Green dress with yellow underskirt; brown shawl; black hat with yellow bow and ribbon; brown basket with purple, pink and yellow flowers
Issued: 1977 - unknown
Series: Old London Streets

Name	U.S. $	Can. $	U.K. £
Flower Seller (Style One)	300.00	350.00	175.00

Flower Seller (The)
Style Two

Designer: Robert Worthington
Height: 7", 17.8 cm
Colour: Yellow dress; white apron and mobcap
Issued: 1982 - 1985
Series: Character Collection

Name	U.S. $	Can. $	U.K. £
Flower Seller (Style Two)	300.00	350.00	175.00

Flower Seller
Style Three

Designer: John Bromley
Height: 8 ½", 21.6 cm
Colour: Peach dress with flowered overskirt; straw bonnet; basket of flowers
Issued: 1994 in a limited edition of 9,500
Series: Cries of London

Name	U.S. $	Can. $	U.K. £
Flower Seller (Style Three)	280.00	325.00	160.00

Note: Commissioned by Compton and Woodhouse.

Follow the Bride

Designer: John Bromley
Height: 5", 12.7 cm
Colour: Peach dress
Issued: 1992 - 1994
Series: Wedding Collection

Name	U.S. $	Can. $	U.K. £
Follow the Bride	165.00	245.00	95.00

For Your Wedding

Designer:	Elizabeth Greenshields
Modeller:	Martin Evans
Height:	8", 20.3 cm
Colour:	White dress with pink bow
Issued:	1992 - 1994
Series:	Wedding Collection

Name	U.S. $	Can. $	U.K. £
For Your Wedding	285.00	325.00	165.00

Foxy Lady

Designer:	David Shilling
Modeller:	John Bromley
Height:	8 ¼", 21.0 cm
Colour:	Gold and purple
Issued:	1986 in a limited edition of 1,000
Series:	Designer Series

Name	U.S. $	Can. $	U.K. £
Foxy Lady	600.00	700.00	350.00

Frances

Designer:	John Bromley
Modeller:	John Bromley
Height:	8 ¼", 21.0 cm
Colour:	Yellow
Issued:	1975 - 1979
Varieties:	Also called Eileen; Emma (Style One); The Hostess; Victoria (Style One)
Series:	Ladies of Fashion

Name	U.S. $	Can. $	U.K. £
Frances	300.00	350.00	175.00

Francesca
Style One

Designer:	John Bromley
Height:	Unknown
Colour:	Unknown
Issued:	1987 in a limited edition of 250
Series:	Edwardian Beauties

Name	U.S. $	Can. $	U.K. £
Francesca (Style One)	285.00	325.00	165.00

Photograph not available at press time

Francesca
Style Two

Designer:	Andy Moss
Height:	5", 12.7 cm
Colour:	Purple (porcelain)
Issued:	1996 - 1997
Series:	Beau Monde

Name	U.S. $	Can. $	U.K. £
Francesca (Style Two)	100.00	150.00	57.50

French Knight

Designer:	Robert Worthington
Height:	Unknown
Colour:	Black and purple
Issued:	1977 - unknown

Name	U.S. $	Can. $	U.K. £
French Knight	475.00	550.00	275.00

Friday's Child

Designer:	John Bromley
Height:	5 ½", 14.0 cm
Colour:	Pink, white and brown
Issued:	1989 - 1991
Series:	Children of the Week

Name	U.S. $	Can. $	U.K. £
Friday's Child	250.00	290.00	145.00

Fuchsia

Designer:	Jack Glynn
Height:	3 ½", 8.9 cm
Colour:	Rose-pink dress with pale pink flowered underskirt; gold trim
Issued:	1994 in a limited edition of 15,000
Series:	Fairest Flowers

Name	U.S. $	Can. $	U.K. £
Fuchsia	120.00	140.00	70.00

Note: Commissioned by Compton and Woodhouse.

Gabrielle

Designer:	Elizabeth Greenshields
Modeller:	Unknown
Height:	8", 20.3 cm
Colour:	Rose-pink
Issued:	1994 - 1997
Series:	Ladies of Fashion

Name	U.S. $	Can. $	U.K. £
Gabrielle	235.00	355.00	135.00

Gail
Style One

Designer:	John Bromley
Modeller:	John Bromley
Height:	3 ½", 8.9 cm
Colour:	Pale green dress with flowered border
Issued:	1985 - 1988
Varieties:	Also called Holly (Style One)
Series:	Kensington Collection

Name	U.S. $	Can. $	U.K. £
Gail (Style One)	85.00	100.00	50.00

Gail
Style Two

Designer:	Helen Buckley
Modeller:	Jack Glynn
Height:	6", 15.0 cm
Colour:	Pale blue
Issued:	1995 to the present
Varieties:	Also called Heather (Style Four)
Series:	Ladies of Fashion

Name	U.S. $	Can. $	U.K. £
Gail (Style Two)	195.00	260.00	110.00

Gala Occasion

Designer:	Elizabeth Greenshields
Modeller:	Martin Evans
Height:	7 ¾", 19.7 cm
Colour:	Mauve and lilac (porcelain)
Issued:	1992 - 1994
Series:	Age of Elegance

Name	U.S. $	Can. $	U.K. £
Gala Occasion	340.00	400.00	195.00

Garden Party (The)

Designer: Helen Buckley
Modeller: John Bromley
Height: 5", 12.7 cm
Colour: Pink and blue
Issued: 1989 to the present
Varieties: Also called May Ball
Series: Debutante Collection

Name	U.S. $	Can. $	U.K. £
Garden Party (The)	100.00	160.00	52.50

Gay Nineties (The)

Designer: John Bromley
Height: 8 ½", 21.6 cm
Colour: Lady - pink dress with black bows
Gentleman - black tuxedo; white shirt
Issued: 1981 - 1984
Series: Dancing Years

Name	U.S. $	Can. $	U.K. £
Gay Nineties (The)	430.00	490.00	245.00

Gemma
Style One

Designer: John Bromley
Modeller: John Bromley
Height: 8", 20.3 cm
Colour: Dark peach
Issued: 1986 - 1989
Varieties: Also called Stella (Style One)
Series: Ladies of Fashion

Name	U.S. $	Can. $	U.K. £
Gemma (Style One)	285.00	325.00	165.00

Gemma
Style Two

Designer:	Unknown
Modeller:	Martin Evans
Height:	3 ½", 8.9 cm
Colour:	Pale green and pink
Issued:	1995 - 1997
Series:	Minuettes

Name	U.S. $	Can. $	U.K. £
Gemma (Style Two)	50.00	89.00	30.00

Georgina
Style One

Designer:	John Bromley
Modeller:	John Bromley
Height:	8 ½", 21.6 cm
Colour:	Yellow and cream
Issued:	1975 - 1979
Varieties:	Also called Alice; Fiona (Style One)
Series:	Ladies of Fashion

Name	U.S. $	Can. $	U.K. £
Georgina (Style One)	325.00	375.00	185.00

Georgina
Style Two

Designer:	Unknown
Modeller:	Martin Evans
Height:	5", 12.7 cm
Colour:	Pale pink and blue
Issued:	1996 - 1997
Series:	Beau Monde

Name	U.S. $	Can. $	U.K. £
Georgina (Style Two)	100.00	150.00	57.50

Georgina Takes Tea With Lady Alice

Designer:	Shirley Curzon
Modeller:	John Bromley
Height:	8 ¼", 21.0 cm
Colour:	Pale pink and white dress and hat
Issued:	1989 in a limited edition of 12,500
Series:	Golden Age

Name	U.S. $	Can. $	U.K. £
Georgina Takes Tea With Lady Alice	225.00	260.00	130.00

Note: Commissioned by Compton and Woodhouse.

Geraldine

Designer:	John Bromley
Modeller:	John Bromley
Height:	8", 20.3 cm
Colour:	Peach with brown highlights
Issued:	1986 - 1991
Varieties:	Also called My Pearl Wedding Day; My Ruby Wedding Day; My Silver Wedding Day
Series:	Ladies of Fashion

Name	U.S. $	Can. $	U.K. £
Geraldine	285.00	325.00	165.00

Gift of Love

Designer:	Timothy Potts
Height:	8 ¼", 21.0 cm
Colour:	Pink and purple
Issued:	1992 in a limited edition of 2,000
Series:	Togetherness

Name	U.S. $	Can. $	U.K. £
Gift of Love	425.00	490.00	245.00

Gillian
Style One

Designer: John Bromley
Modeller: John Bromley
Height: 8", 20.3 cm
Colour: Blue
Issued: 1975 - 1979
Varieties: Also called Debbie; Linda (Style One); Melody; Philippa (Style One)
Series: Ladies of Fashion

Name	U.S. $	Can. $	U.K. £
Gillian (Style One)	285.00	325.00	165.00

Photograph not available at press time

Gillian
Style Two

Designer: John Bromley
Height: 8", 20.3 cm
Colour: Unknown
Issued: 1985
Series: Ladies of Fashion

Name	U.S. $	Can. $	U.K. £
Gillian (Style Two)	225.00	260.00	130.00

Note: Commissioned by Grattan Home Shopping.

Gillian
Style Three

Designer: Graham Miller
Modeller: Graham Miller
Height: 10", 25.4 cm
Colour: Pale blue
Issued: 1993 to the present
Varieties: Also called Eleanor (Style Two)
Series: Silhouettes

Name	U.S. $	Can. $	U.K. £
Gillian (Style Three)	150.00	235.00	72.50

Gilly

Designer:	John Bromley
Height:	8 ½", 21.6 cm
Colour:	White dress with gold highlights
Issued:	1991 - 1992
Varieties:	Also called Miss 1928
Series:	The Roaring Twenties (Style One)

Name	U.S. $	Can. $	U.K. £
Gilly	285.00	325.00	165.00

Gina

Designer:	John Bromley
Height:	9", 22.9 cm
Colour:	Green and brown
Issued:	1985 - 1987
Series:	High Style Collection

Name	U.S. $	Can. $	U.K. £
Gina	475.00	550.00	275.00

Girl Guides Association (1910 - 1985)

Designer:	John Bromley
Height:	5 ½", 14.0 cm
Colour:	Blue
Issued:	1985 - 1985

Name	U.S. $	Can. $	U.K. £
Girl Guides Association	340.00	400.00	195.00

Note: Commissioned to celebrate the 75th Anniversary of the Girl Guides Association.

Girl With Afghan

Designer:	Pauline Shone
Height:	9 ¾", 24.7 cm
Colour:	White dress; light and dark brown dog
Issued:	1979 - unknown
Series:	Children Studies

Name	U.S. $	Can. $	U.K. £
Girl With Afghan	300.00	350.00	175.00

Girl With Fan

Designer:	Alan E. Harmer
Height:	Unknown
Colour:	White, yellow and black
Issued:	1979 - unknown
Series:	Japanese Studies

Name	U.S. $	Can. $	U.K. £
Girl With Fan	340.00	400.00	195.00

Girl With Mask

Designer:	Alan E. Harmer
Height:	Unknown
Colour:	White, yellow and black
Issued:	1979 - unknown
Series:	Japanese Studies

Name	U.S. $	Can. $	U.K. £
Girl With Mask	340.00	400.00	195.00

Girl With Paddington Bear

Designer: Pauline Shone
Height: 10 ¼", 26.0 cm
Colour: White
Issued: 1979 - unknown
Series: Children Studies

Name	U.S. $	Can. $	U.K. £
Girl With Paddington Bear	395.00	450.00	225.00

Girl with Staffordshire Bull Terrier

Designer: Pauline Shone
Height: Unknown
Colour: White dress; dark brown dog
Issued: 1979 - unknown
Series: Children Studies

Name	U.S. $	Can. $	U.K. £
Girl with Staffordshire Bull Terrier	300.00	350.00	175.00

Girl With Yorkshire Terrier

Designer: Pauline Shone
Height: 9 ¼", 23.5 cm
Colour: White dress; brown dog
Issued: 1979 - unknown
Series: Children Studies

Name	U.S.$	Can. $	U.K. £
Girl With Yorkshire Terrier	300.00	350.00	175.00

Note: Original issue price £35.50.

Giselle
Style One

Designer: Unknown
Height: Unknown
Colour: Unknown
Issued: 1982 - 1983
Series: Little Women

Name	U.S. $	Can. $	U.K. £
Giselle (Style One)	165.00	190.00	95.00

Photograph not available at press time

Giselle
Style Two

Designer: John Bromley
Modeller: John Bromley
Height: 5", 12.7 cm
Colour: Yellow and brown
Issued: 1982 - 1986
Varieties: Also called Danielle (Style Two); June (Style Three); Karen (Style One); Michelle (Style Two)
Series: Debutante Collection

Name	U.S. $	Can. $	U.K. £
Giselle (Style Two)	165.00	190.00	95.00

Glamour

Designer: Elizabeth Greenshields
Modeller: John Bromley
Height: 7 ¼", 18.4 cm
Colour: White dress with gold highlights
Issued: 1991 - 1993
Varieties Also called Caress
Series: Chantilly Lace

Name	U.S. $	Can. $	U.K. £
Glamour	285.00	350.00	165.00

Glenda

Designer:	John Bromley
Modeller:	John Bromley
Height:	8 ½", 21.6 cm
Colour:	Purple dress with flowers
Issued:	1987 - 1990
Varieties:	Also called Adele; Melissa
Series:	Ladies of Fashion

Name	U.S. $	Can. $	U.K. £
Glenda	300.00	345.00	175.00

Goddess of the Sun

Designer:	Unknown
Height:	11 ½", 29.2 cm
Colour:	Blue and gold
Issued:	1994 in a limited edition of 5,000

Name	U.S. $	Can. $	U.K. £
Goddess of the Sun	300.00	350.00	175.00

Note: Commissioned by Compton and Woodhouse.

Goose Girl (The)
Style One

Designer:	John Bromley
Height:	7 ¾", 19.7 cm
Colour:	Peach and white dress; green apron; white goose
Issued:	1985 in a limited edition of 1,000
Series:	Arcadian Collection

Name	U.S. $	Can. $	U.K. £
Goose Girl (Style One)	340.00	400.00	195.00

Goose Girl, (The)
Style Two

Designer: Unknown
Height: 5 ½", 14.0 cm
Colour: Pale blue dress; yellow hair; white goose
Issued: 1987 in a limited edition of 5,000

Name	U.S. $	Can. $	U.K. £
Goose Girl (Style Two)	395.00	450.00	225.00

Note: Commissioned by Compton and Woodhouse and issued to commemorate the 200th anniversary of the Brothers Grimm. Original issue price £78.00

Grace
Style One

Designer: John Bromley
Modeller: John Bromley
Height: 5 ¼", 13.3 cm
Colour: Burgundy coat and cream underskirt
Issued: 1984 - 1988
Varieties: Also called Eleanor (Style One); Penelope (Style Two)
Series: Debutante Collection

Name	U.S. $	Can. $	U.K. £
Grace (Style One)	165.00	190.00	95.00

Grace
Style Two

Designer: Unknown
Modeller: Martin Evans
Height: 8 ½", 21.6 cm
Colour: White
Issued: 1993 in a limited edition of 9,500
Series: Golden Age

Name	U.S. $	Can. $	U.K. £
Grace (Style Two)	230.00	265.00	135.00

Note: Commissioned by Compton and Woodhouse.

Grace
Style Three

Designer:	Unknown
Modeller:	Martin Evans
Height:	3 ¾", 9.5 cm
Colour:	Pale green
Issued:	1996 to the present
Varieties:	Also called Leanne
Series:	Minuettes

Name	U.S. $	Can. $	U.K. £
Grace (Style Three)	50.00	99.00	30.00

Graceful

Designer:	Elizabeth Greenshields
Modeller:	John Bromley
Height:	7 ¼", 18.4 cm
Colour:	White and pale lavender
Issued:	1991 - 1993
Varieties:	Also called Breeze (Style Two)
Series:	Chantilly Lace

Name	U.S. $	Can. $	U.K. £
Graceful	285.00	325.00	165.00

Gracious Lily

Designer:	Helen Buckley
Modeller:	Jack Glynn
Height:	8", 20.3 cm
Colour:	Peach and yellow
Issued:	1997 in a limited edition of 250
Varieties:	Also called Enchanted Lily; Fairest Lily
Series:	Flower Ladies

Name	U.S. $	Can. $	U.K. £
Gracious Lily	N/A	445.00	N/A

Note: Commissioned exclusively for the Canadian market.

Graduate Boy (The)

Designer: John Bromley
Height: 8 ¾", 22.2 cm
Colour: Black, white and grey
Issued: 1979 - 1981

Name	U.S. $	Can. $	U.K. £
Graduate Boy (The)	285.00	325.00	165.00

Graduate Girl (The)

Designer: John Bromley
Height: 8 ¼", 21.0 cm
Colour: Black and white
Issued: 1979 - 1981

Name	U.S. $	Can. $	U.K. £
Graduate Girl (The)	285.00	325.00	165.00

Grand Entrance

Designer: John Bromley
Modeller: John Bromley
Height: 8 ¼", 21.0 cm
Colour: Peach
Issued: 1989 - 1993
Series: Ladies of Fashion

Name	U.S. $	Can. $	U.K. £
Grand Entrance	250.00	290.00	145.00

Grand Parade

Designer:	Elizabeth Greenshields
Modeller:	Martin Evans
Height:	8 ¼", 21.0 cm
Colour:	Grey (porcelain)
Issued:	1991 - 1992
Series:	Age of Elegance

Name	U.S. $	Can. $	U.K. £
Grand Parade	285.00	325.00	165.00

Great Ormond Street Nurse

Designer:	John Bromley
Height:	8", 20.3 cm
Colour:	Unknown
Issued:	1985 in a limited edition of 500
Series:	Nurses

Name	U.S. $	Can. $	U.K. £
Great Ormond Street Nurse	240.00	295.00	150.00

Photograph not available at press time

Green (The)

Designer:	John Bromley
Height:	5 ½", 14.0 cm
Colour:	White
Issued:	1986 - 1987
Varieties:	Also called The Crown
Series:	Sporting Collection

Name	U.S. $	Can. $	U.K. £
Green (The)	385.00	440.00	220.00

Greeting (The)

Designer: John Bromley
Modeller: John Bromley
Height: 8 ¼", 21.0 cm
Colour: Yellow
Issued: 1989 - 1990
Series: Ladies of Fashion

Name	U.S. $	Can. $	U.K. £
Greeting (The)	250.00	290.00	145.00

Photograph not available at press time

Grenadier Guard

Designer: Unknown
Height: 10 ¼", 26.0 cm
Colour: Red tunic; black trousers and bearskin
Issued: 1980 - 1980
Series: London Heritage

Name	U.S. $	Can. $	U.K. £
Grenadier Guard	300.00	350.00	175.00

Greta

Designer: Elizabeth Greenshields
Modeller: Unknown
Height: 8", 20.3 cm
Colour: Peach
Issued: 1992 - 1993
Series: West End Girls

Name	U.S. $	Can. $	U.K. £
Greta	340.00	400.00	195.00

Groom (The)

Designer:	Unknown
Height:	5 ¼", 13.5 cm
Colour:	Light grey
Issued:	1983 - 1985
Series:	Wedding Collection

Name	U.S. $	Can. $	U.K. £
Groom (The)	150.00	175.00	85.00

Gwen

Designer:	John Bromley
Modeller:	John Bromley
Height:	5", 12.7 cm
Colour:	White with gold trim
Issued:	1985 - 1990
Varieties:	Also called Jill (Style One); Mary (Style One); Tracy; Vivienne
Series:	Debutante Collection

Name	U.S. $	Can. $	U.K. £
Gwen	140.00	160.00	80.00

Hamlet

Designer:	Robert Worthington
Height:	7 ¼", 18.4 cm
Colour:	Purple
Issued:	1981 in a limited edition of 2,000
Series:	Characters from Shakespeare

Name	U.S. $	Can. $	U.K. £
Hamlet	395.00	450.00	225.00

Hannah
Style One

Designer: John Bromley
Modeller: John Bromley
Height: 5 ¼", 13.3 cm
Colour: Pale tan with dark brown highlights
Issued: 1985 - 1988
Varieties: Also called Beatrice (Style One); Prudence
Series: Debutante Collection

Name	U.S. $	Can. $	U.K. £
Hannah (Style One)	165.00	190.00	95.00

Hannah
Style Two

Designer: Unknown
Modeller: Martin Evans
Height: 3 ½", 8.9 cm
Colour: Turquoise
Issued: 1995 to the present
Varieties: Also called Michelle (Style Three); Summertime
Series: Minuettes

Name	U.S. $	Can. $	U.K. £
Hannah (Style Two)	50.00	69.50	30.00

Happy Anniversary

Designer: Helen Buckley
Modeller: John Bromley
Height: 8 ¼", 21.0 cm
Colour: Pink and lavender
Issued: 1991 - 1994
Series: Ladies of Fashion

Name	U.S. $	Can. $	U.K. £
Happy Anniversary	285.00	310.00	165.00

Happy Birthday

Designer: Elizabeth Greenshields
Modeller: John Bromley
Height: 8", 20.3 cm
Colour: White and pink
Issued: 1992 - 1995
Series: Ladies of Fashion

Name	U.S. $	Can. $	U.K. £
Happy Birthday	285.00	350.00	165.00

Harlequin

Designer: Unknown
Height: 9 ½", 24.0 cm
Colour: Multi-coloured
Issued: 1983 in a limited edition of 100

Name	U.S. $	Can. $	U.K. £
Harlequin	775.00	900.00	450.00

Note: Commissioned by Terrys Chocolates.

Harmony

Designer: John Bromley
Modeller: John Bromley
Height: 8 ½", 21.6 cm
Colour: Dark green jacket and skirt trimmed with fur
Issued: 1987 - 1992
Varieties: Also called Sophie (Style Two)
Series: Ladies of Fashion

Name	U.S. $	Can. $	U.K. £
Harmony	250.00	290.00	145.00

Annette (Style One) in two colourways
Green model c.1920 with a black backstamp
Blue model c.1949 with a green backstamp

Daisy (Style One) in two colourways
Blue model with a green backstamp
Yellow model with a black backstamp

Peggy in two colourways
Blue hat model with a green backstamp
Black hat model with a black backstamp

Miss Julie in two colourways
Both models with black backstamps

Judith Ann in two colourways
She is a reblocked figurine issued in 1973

Rosalinda in two colourways
Model on the left is a reblocked model issued in 1973
Model on the right was issued c.1949

Rosalinda (left) and Barbara (right) were issued in 1973 and both are reblocked models

Jennifer Jane (left) and Judith Ann (right) were issued in 1973 and both are reblocked models

The Music Seller, The News Sheet Seller, The Pie Maker, The Suffragette, The Medicine Man, Flower Seller (Style Two)

Eileen and The Hostess
Same model in different colourways

Grace and Eleanor
Same model in different colourways

From left to right: Catherine Parr, Anne of Cleves, Anne Boleyn from the Royal Collection

From left to right: Katherine Howard, Jane Seymour, Catherine of Aragon from the Royal Collection

Red Rose of Lancashire
Commissioned by Peter Jones China Ltd.

Wakefield Rose
Commissioned by Peter JonesChina Ltd.

Lady Caroline at the Summer Garden Party
Commissioned by Compton and Woodhouse

Lady Helena Riding in Hyde Park
Commissioned by Compton and Woodhouse

Blue Moon

Lady Sylvia

ENGLISH ROSE SERIES

May Queen

Marlena

Pretty Jessica

Sweet Juliet

ENGLISH ROSE SERIES

English Elegance

Moonlight

The Letter
Issued in a limited edition of 250

Harriet

Designer: Elizabeth Greenshields
Modeller: Brian Diment
Height: 5 ¼", 13.3 cm
Colour: Blue (porcelain)
Issued: 1992 - 1994
Series: Beau Monde

Name	U.S. $	Can. $	U.K. £
Harriet	195.00	220.00	110.00

Photograph not available at press time

Hayley

Designer: Helen Buckley
Modeller: John Bromley
Height: 6 ½", 16.5 cm
Colour: Light green dress and hat; dark green shawl
Issued: 1987 to the present
Series: Ladies of Fashion

Name	U.S. $	Can. $	U.K. £
Hayley	265.00	445.00	150.00

Hazel

Designer: Elizabeth Greenshields
Modeller: Martin Evans
Height: 8 ½", 21.6 cm
Colour: Turquoise
Issued: 1986 - unknown
Varieties: Also called Julie (Style Two)
Series: Ladies of Fashion

Name	U.S. $	Can. $	U.K. £
Hazel	195.00	220.00	110.00

Heather
Style One

Designer:	John Bromley
Modeller:	John Bromley
Height:	8", 20.3 cm
Colour:	Emerald green dress; white underskirt
Issued:	1977 - 1982
Varieties:	Also called Alison; Emily; Flair; Henrietta
Series:	Ladies of Fashion

Name	U.S. $	Can. $	U.K. £
Heather (Style One)	300.00	350.00	175.00

Heather
Style Two

Designer:	Helen Buckley
Modeller:	John Bromley
Height:	8 ½", 21.6 cm
Colour:	White and pink
Issued:	1988 - 1990
Series:	Ladies of Fashion

Name	U.S. $	Can. $	U.K. £
Heather (Style Two)	280.00	325.00	160.00

Heather
Style Three

Designer:	Jack Glynn
Height:	3 ½", 8.9 cm
Colour:	Purple and green overdress; pale green underskirt with purple flowers; green hat; basket of flowers
Isssued:	1993 in a limited edition of 15,000
Series:	Fairest Flowers

Name	U.S. $	Can. $	U.K. £
Heather (Style Three)	125.00	140.00	70.00

Note: Commissioned by Compton and Woodhouse.

Heather
Style Four

Designer: Jack Glynn
Height: 6", 15.0 cm
Colour: Pink
Issued: 1996
Varieties: Also called Gail (Style Two)
Series: Ladies of Fashion

Name	U.S. $	Can. $	U.K. £
Heather (Style Four)	175.00	200.00	99.95

Note: Commissioned by Freemans Home Shopping.

Helen
Style One

Designer: John Bromley
Modeller: John Bromley
Height: 7 ½", 19.1 cm
Colour: Green
Issued: 1977 - 1982
Varieties: Also called Constance
Series: Ladies of Fashion

Name	U.S. $	Can. $	U.K. £
Helen (Style One)	300.00	350.00	175.00

Helen
Style Two

Designer: Elizabeth Greenshields
Modeller: Unknown
Height: 8 ¼", 21.0 cm
Colour: Beige dress; green hat
Issued: 1994 - 1994
Series: Special Events

Name	U.S. $	Can. $	U.K. £
Helen (Style Two)	340.00	495.00	195.00

Helen of Troy
(on wooden plinth)

Designer: David Cornell
Height: 9 ¼", 23.5 cm
Colour: White dress with gold trimming; lilac shawl
Issued: 1995 in a limited edition of 9,500
Series: Fabled Beauties

Name	U.S. $	Can. $	U.K. £
Helen of Troy	300.00	350.00	175.00

Note: Commissioned by Compton and Woodhouse.

Helping Hand (A)

Designer: Timothy Potts
Height: 8 ¼", 21.0 cm
Colour: Mother in pink dress; boy in blue and white sailor suit
Issued: 1994 in a limited edition of 2,000
Series: Togetherness

Name	U.S. $	Can. $	U.K. £
Helping Hand (A)	395.00	450.00	225.00

Henley Royal Regatta

Designer: Elizabeth Greenshields
Modeller: Brian Diment
Height: 9 ½", 24.0 cm
Colour: Yellow and blue (porcelain)
Issued: 1994 in a limited edition of 2,000
Series: Turn of the Century

Name	U.S. $	Can. $	U.K. £
Henley Royal Regatta	525.00	650.00	295.00

Henrietta

Designer:	John Bromley
Modeller:	John Bromley
Height:	8", 20.3 cm
Colour:	Pale green dress; white underskirt
Issued:	1977 - 1995
Varieties:	Also called Alison; Emily; Flair; Heather (Style One)
Series:	Ladies of Fashion

Name	U.S. $	Can. $	U.K. £
Henrietta	250.00	300.00	145.00

Henry IV

Designer:	Robert Worthington
Height:	7 ½", 19.1 cm
Colour:	Maroon and purple
Issued:	1979 in a limited edition of 2,000
Series:	Characters from Shakespeare

Name	U.S. $	Can. $	U.K. £
Henry IV	425.00	500.00	250.00

Henry V

Designer:	Unknown
Modeller:	Robert Worthington
Height:	10 ½", 26.7 cm
Colour:	Blue and red
Issued:	1979 in a limited edition of 2,000
Series:	Characters from Shakespeare

Name	U.S $	Can. $	U.K. £
Henry V	425.00	490.00	245.00

Henry VIII

Designer:	Unknown
Modeller:	Robert Worthington
Height:	9", 22.9 cm
Colour:	Red, brown and beige
Issued:	1979 - 1992
Series:	Royal Collection

Name	U.S. $	Can. $	U.K. £
Henry VIII	675.00	800.00	395.00

High Society
Style One

Designer:	John Bromley
Modeller:	John Bromley
Height:	8 ½", 21.6 cm
Colour:	Peach
Issued:	1988 - 1993
Varieties:	Also called Lauren (Style One)
Series:	Ladies of Fashion

Name	U.S. $	Can. $	U.K. £
High Society (Style One)	300.00	350.00	175.00

High Society
Style Two

Designer:	John Bromley
Height:	9 ½", 24.0 cm
Colour:	Ivory
Issued:	1991 in a limited edition of 12,500
Series:	Screen Goddesses

Name	U.S. $	Can. $	U.K. £
High Society (Style Two)	175.00	200.00	100.00

Note: Commissioned by Compton and Woodhouse.

High Style

Designer:	Elizabeth Greenshields
Modeller:	John Bromley
Height:	7 ¼", 18.4 cm
Colour:	Mauve dress; purple hat
Issued:	1992 - 1993
Varieties:	Also called Dignity; Lace
Series:	Chantilly Lace

Name	U.S. $	Can. $	U.K. £
High Style	250.00	290.00	145.00

Holly
Style One

Designer:	John Bromley
Modeller:	John Bromley
Height:	3 ½", 8.9 cm
Colour:	Pale pink
Issued:	1985 - 1988
Varieties:	Also called Gail (Style One)
Series:	Kensington Collection

Name	U.S. $	Can. $	U.K. £
Holly (Style One)	85.00	100.00	50.00

Holly
Style Two

Designer:	Jack Glynn
Height:	3 ½", 8.9 cm
Colour:	Green overdress with gold holly design; cream underskirt; green hat with red bow and ribbon; gold trim
Issued:	1993 in a limited edition of 15,000
Series:	Fairest Flowers

Name	U.S. $	Can. $	U.K. £
Holly (Style Two)	125.00	140.00	70.00

Note: Commissioned by Compton and Woodhouse.

Holly
Style Three

Designer: Martin Evans
Height: 3 ¾", 9.5 cm
Colour: Mauve
Issued: 1995 to the present
Varieties: Also called Zoe (Style Two)
Series: Minuettes

Name	U.S. $	Can. $	U.K. £
Holly (Style Three)	50.00	79.50	30.00

Honeymoon

Designer: John Bromley
Modeller: John Bromley
Height: 8 ¼", 21.0 cm
Colour: Green and yellow
Issued: 1991 - 1993
Series: Ladies of Fashion

Name	U.S. $	Can. $	U.K. £
Honeymoon	285.00	325.00	165.00

Honor

Designer: Helen Buckley
Modeller: John Bromley
Height: 7 ¾", 19.7 cm
Colour: Pale blue
Issued: 1986 - 1990
Series: Ladies of Fashion

Name	U.S. $	Can. $	U.K. £
Honor	300.00	395.00	175.00

Hostess (The)

Designer: John Bromley
Modeller: John Bromley
Height: 8 ¼", 21.0 cm
Colour: White floral pattern
Issued: 1977 - 1980
Varieties: Also called Eileen; Emma (Style One); Frances; Victoria (Style One)
Series: Ladies of Fashion

Name	U.S. $	Can. $	U.K. £
Hostess (The)	340.00	400.00	195.00

House of Hanover (1727-1760)

Designer: Unknown
Height: 6 ½", 16.5 cm
Colour: Jade dress with gold and turquoise design; white bodice, apron and cap
Issued: 1979 in a limited edition of 500
Series: History of Costume

Name	U.S. $	Can. $	U.K. £
House of Hanover (1727-1760)	650.00	750.00	375.00

House of Hanover (1790-1837)

Designer: John Bromley
Height: 11 ½", 29.2 cm
Colour: White dress with red ribbon and rose
Issued: 1981 in a limited edition of 500
Series: History of Costume

Name	U.S. $	Can. $	U.K. £
House of Hanover (1790-1837)	950.00	1,100.00	550.00

House of Hanover, Empire Style (1804-1815)

Designer:	Douglas Tootle
Height:	10 ¾", 27.8 cm
Colour:	White dress and shawl with gold highlights
Issued:	1984 in a limited edition of 500
Series:	History of Costume

Name	U.S. $	Can. $	U.K. £
Empire Style (1804-1815)	825.00	950.00	475.00

House of Hanover, George II (1745-1755)

Designer:	John Bromley
Height:	10 ¾", 27.8 cm
Colour:	Grey-blue dress trimmed with beige; beige hat with red and white ribbon
Issued:	1980 in a limited edition of 500
Series:	History of Costume

Name	U.S. $	Can. $	U.K. £
House of Hanover (1745-1755)	950.00	1,100.00	550.00

House of Hanover, Victoria (1837-1856)

Designer:	Douglas Tootle
Height:	10 ½", 26.7 cm
Colour:	White and peach
Issued:	1984 in a limited edition of 500
Series:	History of Costume

Name	U.S. $	Can. $	U.K. £
House of Hanover (1837-1856)	900.00	1,000.00	525.00

House of Lancaster (1399-1461)

Designer:	John Bromley
Height:	10 ¼", 26.0 cm
Colour:	Peach and mauve
Issued:	1979 in a limited edition of 500
Series:	History of Costume

Name	U.S. $	Can. $	U.K. £
House of Lancaster (1399-1461)	950.00	1,100.00	550.00

House of Norman (1066-1154)

Designer:	John Bromley
Height:	10", 25.4 cm
Colour:	Beige dress; blue cape; white headdress
Issued:	1979 in a limited edition of 500
Series:	History of Costume

Name	U.S. $	Can. $	U.K. £
House of Norman (1066-1154)	690.00	800.00	395.00

House of Plantagenet (1350-1399)

Designer:	Douglas Tootle
Height:	10 ¾", 27.8 cm
Colour:	Yellow and white
Issued:	1984 in a limited edition of 500
Series:	History of Costume

Name	U.S. $	Can. $	U.K. £
House of Plantagenet (1350-1399)	830.00	950.00	475.00

House of Plantagenet, Edward II (1307-1327)

Designer:	John Bromley
Height:	10", 25.4 cm
Colour:	Purple, pink, white and gold
Issued:	1979 in a limited edition of 500
Series:	History of Costume

Name	U.S. $	Can. $	U.K. £
House of Plantagenet (1307-1327)	900.00	1,000.00	525.00

House of Stuart (1603 - 1714)

Designer:	Douglas Tootle
Height:	10 ½", 26.7 cm
Colour:	Navy and sky blue
Issued:	1984 in a limited edition of 500
Series:	History of Costume

Name	U.S. $	Can. $	U.K. £
House of Stuart (1603-1714)	825.00	950.00	475.00

House of Stuart (1625 - 1649)

Designer:	Unknown
Height:	6 ½", 16.5 cm
Colour:	Green dress; brown shawl
Issued:	1980 in a limited edition of 500
Series:	History of Costume

Name	U.S. $	Can. $	U.K. £
House of Stuart (1625-1649)	775.00	900.00	450.00

Photograph not available at press time

House of Stuart, James I (1603 - 1625)

Designer: John Bromley
Height: 10 ¼", 26.0 cm
Colour: Dark pink
Issued: 1979 in a limited edition of 500
Series: History of Costume

Name	U.S. $	Can. $	U.K. £
House of Stuart, James I (1603 - 1625)	900.00	1,100.00	525.00

House of Tudor (1485-1603)

Designer: Douglas Tootle
Height: 10 ¼", 26.0 cm
Colour: Peach and gold
Issued: 1984 in a limited edition of 500
Series: History of Costume

Name	U.S. $	Can. $	U.K. £
House of Tudor (1485-1603)	825.00	900.00	475.00

House of Tudor (1558-1603)

Designer: John Bromley
Height: 10 ¼", 26.0 cm
Colour: Green
Issued: 1980 in a limited edition of 500
Series: History of Costume

Name	U.S. $	Can. $	U.K. £
House of Tudor (1558-1603)	875.00	1,000.00	500.00

Photograph not available at press time

House of York (1461-1485)

Designer:	Douglas Tootle
Height:	10 ½", 26.7 cm
Colour:	Green and gold
Issued:	1984 in a limited edition of 500
Series:	History of Costume

Name	U.S. $	Can. $	U.K. £
House of York (1461-1485)	825.00	900.00	475.00

H.M. Queen Elizabeth II
Style Two

Designer:	Unknown
Height:	8 ½ ", 21.6 cm
Colour:	Ivory dress; purple cloak trimmed with ermine; purple crown trimmed with ermine and gold; gold jewellery
Issued:	1996 in a limited edition of 500
Series:	Royalty

Name	U.S. $	Can. $	U.K. £
H.M. Queen Elizabeth II (Style Two)	250.00	300.00	150.00

Note: Commissioned by Peter Jones China Ltd., Wakefield, to celebrate the 70th birthday of Her Majesty The Queen.

H.M. Queen Elizabeth II and H.R.H. Duke of Edinburgh

Designer:	Unknown
Height:	9 ½ ", 24.0 cm
Colour:	Queen — Pink gown; blue sash; gold jewellery Prince Philip — Red tunic with gold embellishments; blue sash; black trousers
Issued:	1997 in a limited edition of 250
Series:	Royalty

Name	U.S. $	Can. $	U.K. £
H.M. Queen Elizabeth II and H.R.H. Duke of Edinburgh	500.00	600.00	285.00

Note: Commissioned by Peter Jones China Ltd., Wakefield , to celebrate the 50th wedding anniversary of The Queen and Prince Philip.

H.M. Queen Elizabeth, The Queen Mother
Style Two

Designer: Unknown
Height: 8 ½ ", 21.6 cm
Colour: Ivory dress; blue sash
Issued: 1995 in a limited edition of 500
Series: Royal Figures

Name	U.S. $	Can. $	U.K. £
H.M. Queen Elizabeth, The Queen Mother	250.00	300.00	150.00

Note: Commissioned by Peter Jones China Ltd., Wakefield, to celebrate the 95th birthday of The Queen Mother.

H.R.H The Prince of Wales
Style One

Designer: Colin Melbourne
Height: 8 ¾", 22.2 cm
Colour: Cream shirt; green kilt
Issued: 1981 in a limited edition of 1,000
Series: Royalty

Name	U.S. $	Can. $	U.K. £
H.R.H The Prince of Wales (Style One)	300.00	350.00	175.00

H.R.H The Prince of Wales
Style Two

Designer: Unknown
Height: 8 ¾", 22.2 cm
Colour: Khaki
Issued: Unknown, in a limited edition of 1,000
Series: Royalty

Name	U.S. $	Can. $	U.K. £
H.R.H The Prince of Wales (Style Two)	265.00	300.00	150.00

Hyacinth

Designer: Jack Glynn
Height: 3 ½", 8.9 cm
Colour: Dark blue overdress; light blue underskirt with flowered border; gold trim
Issued: 1993 in a limited edition of 15,000
Series: Fairest Flowers

Name	U.S. $	Can. $	U.K. £
Hyacinth	125.00	140.00	69.00

Note: Commissioned by Compton and Woodhouse.

Hyde Park

Designer: Elizabeth Greenshields
Modeller: Martin Evans
Height: 8 ¼", 21.0 cm
Colour: Pale lavender and purple
Issued: 1993 to the present
Series: Age of Elegance

Name	U.S. $	Can. $	U.K. £
Hyde Park	250.00	325.00	145.00

I Love Kitty

Designer: John Bromley
Height: 4 ½", 11.5 cm
Colour: Pale blue pyjamas; black cat
Issued: 1980 - unknown
Series: Children Studies

Name	U.S. $	Can. $	U.K. £
I Love Kitty	280.00	325.00	160.00

In Love

Designer:	John Bromley
Height:	4", 10.1 cm
Colour:	Rose-pink
Issued:	1989 to the present
Varieties:	Also called Fascination
Series:	Debutante Collection

Name	U.S. $	Can. $	U.K. £
In Love	100.00	150.00	52.50

In Vogue

Designer:	John Bromley
Modeller:	John Bromley
Height:	5", 12.7 cm
Colour:	Blue
Issued:	1991 - 1994
Series:	Debutante Collection

Name	U.S. $	Can. $	U.K. £
In Vogue	130.00	150.00	80.00

Innocence

Designer:	David Lyttleton
Height:	7 ¼", 18.4 cm
Colour:	Pale blue dress; brown and red bird
Issued:	1992 in a limited edition of 5,000
Series:	Barnardo's

Name	U.S. $	Can. $	U.K. £
Innocence	165.00	190.00	90.00

Note: Commissioned by Compton and Woodhouse.

Interlude

Designer: Elizabeth Greenshields
Modeller: Brian Diment
Height: 7 ½", 19.1 cm
Colour: Pink and pale green (porcelain)
Issued: 1991 - 1993
Series: Age of Elegance

Name	U.S. $	Can. $	U.K. £
Interlude	285.00	325.00	165.00

Invitation to the Ball

Designer: John Bromley
Modeller: John Bromley
Height: 8", 20.3 cm
Colour: Peach
Issued: 1983 - 1986
Series: Ladies of Fashion

Name	U.S. $	Can. $	U.K. £
Invitation to the Ball	300.00	350.00	175.00

Iris
Style One

Designer: Jack Glynn
Height: 3 ½", 8.9 cm
Colour: Blue overdress, white underskirt with iris flowers; pale blue shawl; gold trim
Issued: 1993 in a limited edition of 15,000
Series: Fairest Flowers

Name	U.S. $	Can. $	U.K. £
Iris (Style One)	125.00	140.00	70.00

Note: Commissioned by Compton and Woodhouse.

Iris
Style Two

Designer:	Jack Glynn
Height:	9", 22.9 cm
Colour:	Pale blue crinoline gown with darker blue bows; bouquet of irises
Issued:	1994 in a limited edition of 12,500
Series:	The Four Flowers Collection

Name	U.S. $	Can. $	U.K. £
Iris (Style Two)	280.00	325.00	158.00

Note: Commissioned by Compton and Woodhouse.

Photograph not available at press time

Isabella
Style One

Designer:	John Bromley
Height:	Unknown
Colour:	Unknown
Issued:	1987 in a limited edition of 250
Series:	Edwardian Beauties

Name	U.S. $	Can. $	U.K. £
Isabella (Style One)	300.00	350.00	175.00

Isabella
Style Two

Designer:	Elizabeth Greenshields
Modeller:	Brian Diment
Height:	5 ¼", 13.3 cm
Colour:	Blue and yellow (porcelain)
Issued:	1992 - 1993
Series:	Beau Monde

Name	U.S. $	Can. $	U.K. £
Isabella (Style Two)	150.00	175.00	110.00

Isadora

Designer: John Bromley
Height: 8 ¾", 22.2 cm
Colour: Pink
Issued: 1977 - 1982
Series: Ladies of Fashion

Name	U.S. $	Can. $	U.K. £
Isadora	300.00	350.00	175.00

Jack Point

Designer: Unknown
Height: Unknown
Colour: Unknown
Issued: 1979 - 1981
Series: Gilbert and Sullivan

Name	U.S. $	Can. $	U.K. £
Jack Point	650.00	750.00	375.00

Photograph not available at press time

Jacqueline Style One

Designer: John Bromley
Modeller: John Bromley
Height: 5", 12.7 cm
Colour: Yellow dress with pink bodice
Issued: 1984 - 1988
Varieties: Also called Christine (Style Two); Elaine (Style One)
Series: Debutante Collection

Name	U.S. $	Can. $	U.K. £
Jacqueline (Style One)	160.00	180.00	90.00

Jacqueline
Style Two

Designer: Elizabeth Greenshields
Modeller: Jack Glynn
Height: 8 ¾", 22.2 cm
Colour: Peach
Issued: 1995 - 1995
Series: Figurine of the Year

Name	U.S. $	Can. $	U.K. £
Jacqueline (Style Two)	280.00	325.00	250.00

Jade

Designer: Unknown
Modeller: Martin Evans
Height: 3 ½", 8.9 cm
Colour: Dark and pale green
Issued: 1996 to the present
Varieties: Also called Rosie (Style Two)
Series: Minuettes

Name	U.S. $	Can. $	U.K. £
Jade	50.00	105.00	30.00

Jan

Designer: Helen Buckley
Modeller: John Bromley
Height: 8 ½", 21.6 cm
Colour: Pale pink and grey
Issued: 1988 - 1990
Series: Ladies of Fashion

Name	U.S. $	Can. $	U.K. £
Jan	285.00	325.00	165.00

Jane
Style One

Designer: John Bromley
Modeller: John Bromley
Height: 8 ¾", 22.2 cm
Colour: Deep pink
Issued: c.1980 - unknown
Varieties: Also called Jayne (Style One)
Series: Ladies of Fashion

Name	U.S. $	Can. $	U.K. £
Jane (Style One)	285.00	325.00	165.00

Jane
Style Two

Designer: Elizabeth Greenshields
Modelle: Martin Evans
Height: 5 ¼", 13.3 cm
Colour: Lavender and cream
Issued: 1994 - 1995
Series: Debutante Collection

Name	U.S. $	Can. $	U.K. £
Jane (Style Two)	130.00	170.00	75.00

Jane Seymour

Designer: Unknown
Modeller: Robert Worthington
Height: 8", 20.3 cm
Colour: Red, white and gold
Issued: 1979 - 1992
Series: Royal Collection

Name	U.S. $	Can. $	U.K. £
Jane Seymour	550.00	650.00	325.00

Janet

Designer:	John Bromley
Modeller:	John Bromley
Height:	7 ¾", 19.7 cm
Colour:	White and pink
Issued:	1984 - 1986
Varieties:	Also called Davina; Moira
Series:	Ladies of Fashion

Name	U.S. $	Can. $	U.K. £
Janet	300.00	350.00	175.00

Janice

Designer:	Helen Buckley
Modeller:	Andy Moss
Height:	3 ¾", 9.5 cm
Colour:	Pale blue
Issued:	1996 to the present
Series:	Debutante Collection

Name	U.S. $	Can. $	U.K. £
Janice	100.00	150.00	52.50

Jasmine

Designer:	Jack Glynn
Height:	3 ½", 8.9 cm
Colour:	Green overdress; white underskirt with yellow flowers; gold trim
Issued:	1993 in a limited edition of 15,000
Series:	Fairest Flowers

Name	U.S. $	Can. $	U.K. £
Jasmine	125.00	140.00	70.00

Note: Commissioned by Compton and Woodhouse.

Jayne
Style One

Designer: John Bromley
Modller: John Bromley
Height: 9", 22.9 cm
Colour: Pale blue
Issued: 1980 - 1986
Varieties: Also called Jane (Style One)
Series: Ladies of Fashion

Name	U.S. $	Can. $	U.K. £
Jayne (Style One)	285.00	325.00	165.00

Jayne
Style Two

Designer: Martin Evans
Modeller: Martin Evans
Height: 5 ¾", 14.6 cm
Colour: Yellow
Issued: 1996
Varieties: Also called Alexandra (Style Two)
Series: Debutante

Name	U.S. $	Can. $	U.K. £
Jayne (Style Two)	85.00	100.00	49.95

Note: Commissioned by Littlewoods Home Shopping.

Jean
Style One

Designer: John Bromley
Modeller: John Bromley
Height: 7", 17.8 cm
Colour: Green dress with white frills
Issued: 1977 - 1982
Varieties: Also called Josephine; Regina; Serenade (Style One); Winsome
Series: Ladies of Fashion

Name	U.S. $	Can. $	U.K. £
Jean (Style One)	300.00	350.00	175.00

Jean
Style Two

Designer:	Helen Buckley
Modeller:	Martin Evans
Height:	7 ¾", 19.7 cm
Colour:	Pale blue and lemon
Issued:	1996 to the present
Varieties:	Also called Lindsey
Series:	Ladies of Fashion

Name	U.S. $	Can. $	U.K. £
Jean (Style Two)	175.00	275.00	110.00

Photograph not available at press time

Jeanette
Style One

Designer:	Unknown
Height:	Unknown
Colour:	Unknown
Issued:	1982 - 1983
Series:	Little Women

Name	U.S. $	Can. $	U.K. £
Jeanette (Style One)	195.00	220.00	110.00

Jeanette
Style Two

Designer:	John Bromley
Modeller:	John Bromley
Height:	5", 12.7 cm
Colour:	White and pink dress with pink flowers
Issued:	1982 - 1986
Varieties:	Also called Annette (Style Four); Claudette (Style Two); Joanne (Style One); Juliette (Style Two); Lynette (Style Two); Sally Anne (Style Two)
Series:	Debutante Collection

Name	U.S. $	Can. $	U.K. £
Jeanette (Style Two)	175.00	200.00	95.00

Jennifer
Style Two

Designer: John Bromley
Modeller: John Bromley
Height: 5", 12.7 cm
Colour: Pale green dress with flowered border
Issued: 1983 - 1990
Varieties: Also called Estelle (Style Two); Nanette (Style Two); Nicolette (Style Two); Paulette (Style Two)
Series: Debutante Collection

Name	U.S. $	Can. $	U.K. £
Jennifer (Style Two)	140.00	160.00	80.00

Jennifer
Style Three

Designer: Helen Buckley
Modeller: Martin Evans
Height: 7 ½", 19.1 cm
Colour: Yellow and pink
Issued: 1996 to the present
Series: Ladies of Fashion

Name	U.S. $	Can. $	U.K. £
Jennifer (Style Three)	165.00	275.00	90.00

Jessica
Style Two

Designer: Unknown
Modeller: Martin Evans
Height: 3 ½", 8.9 cm
Colour: Pink
Issued: 1995 to the present
Varieties: Also called Danielle (Style Two)
Series: Minuettes

Name	U.S. $	Can. $	U.K. £
Jessica (Style Two)	50.00	79.50	30.00

Jill
Style One

Designer: John Bromley
Modeller: John Bromley
Height: 5", 12.7 cm
Colour: Yellow
Issued: 1983 - 1985
Varieties: Also called Gwen; Mary (Style One); Tracy; Vivienne
Series: Debutante Collection

Name	U.S. $	Can. $	U.K. £
Jill (Style One)	165.00	190.00	95.00

Jill
Style Two

Designer: Elizabeth Greenshields
Modeller: Martin Evans
Height: 5 ½", 14.0 cm
Colour: Pale lavender and purple (porcelain)
Issued: 1994 to the present
Series: Beau Monde

Name	U.S. $	Can. $	U.K. £
Jill (Style Two)	125.00	195.00	57.50

Jo

Designer: John Bromley
Height: 5 ½", 14.0 cm
Colour: Pale green
Issued: 1988 - 1991
Series: Debutante Collection

Name	U.S. $	Can. $	U.K. £
Jo	150.00	170.00	85.00

Joan
Style Two

Designer:	Helen Buckley
Modeller:	Jack Glynn
Height:	8", 20.3 cm
Colour:	Brown and pale brown
Issued:	1997 to the present
Series:	Ladies of Fashion

Name	U.S. $	Can. $	U.K. £
Joan (Style Two)	250.00	365.00	125.00

Joanne
Style One

Designer:	John Bromley
Modeller:	John Bromley
Height:	5", 12.7 cm
Colour:	Red
Issued:	1983 - 1990
Varieties:	Also called Annette (Style Four); Claudette (Style Two); Jeanette (Style Two); Juliette (Style Two); Lynette (Style Two); Sally Anne (Style One)
Series:	Debutante Collection

Name	U.S. $	Can. $	U.K. £
Joanne (Style One)	130.00	150.00	75.00

Joanne
Style Two

Designer:	Unknown
Modeller:	Martin Evans
Height:	3 ½", 8.9 cm
Colour:	Pale blue and pink
Issued:	1995 - 1997
Series:	Minuettes

Name	U.S. $	Can. $	U.K. £
Joanne (Style Two)	55.00	99.50	30.00

Jody

Designer:	John Bromley
Height:	9", 22.9 cm
Colour:	Green and brown
Issued:	1985 - 1987
Series:	High Style Collection

Name	U.S. $	Can. $	U.K. £
Jody	475.00	550.00	275.00

Josephine

Designer:	John Bromley
Modeller:	John Bromley
Height:	7", 17.8 cm
Colour:	Gold and white
Issued:	1977 - 1982
Varieties:	Also called Jean (Style One); Regina; Serenade (Style One); Winsome
Series:	Ladies of Fashion

Name	U.S. $	Can. $	U.K. £
Jacqueline	300.00	350.00	175.00

Joy

Designer:	John Bromley
Modeller:	John Bromley
Height:	6 ½", 15.9 cm
Colour:	Pink dress with flowered underskirt
Issued:	1975 - 1987
Varieties:	Also called Angelique; Celeste
Series:	Ladies of Fashion

Name	U.S. $	Can. $	U.K. £
Joy	265.00	300.00	150.00

Judge (The)

Designer: Margaret Whittaker
Height: 7 ½", 19.1 cm
Colour: Black and white robes; brown pedestal
Issued: 1977 - 1981
Series: Gilbert and Sullivan

Name	U.S. $	Can. $	U.K. £
Judge (The)	650.00	750.00	375.00

Julia
Style One

Designer: John Bromley
Modeller: John Bromley
Height: 8", 20.3 cm
Colour: Yellow dress with flowered bodice; green collar and sleeves
Issued: 1984 - 1987
Varieties: Also called Peggy; Sally Anne (Style One)
Series: Ladies of Fashion

Name	U.S. $	Can. $	U.K. £
Julia (Style One)	285.00	325.00	165.00

Julia
Style Two

Designer: Elizabeth Greenshields
Modeller: John Bromley
Height: 7 ¼", 18.4 cm
Colour: Lavender and pink
Issued: 1993 - 1993
Varieties: Also called Attraction; Chloe (Style Two); Demure
Series: Chantilly Lace

Name	U.S. $	Can. $	U.K. £
Julia (Style Two)	340.00	400.00	195.00

Julie
Style One

Designer: John Bromley
Modeller: John Bromley
Height: 7 ½", 19.1 cm
Colour: 1. Red dress; blue spotted underskirt; blue hat
2. Purple
Issued: 1975 - 1977
Varieties: Also called Anne Marie; Louise
Series: Ladies of Fashion

Name	U.S. $	Can. $	U.K. £
Julie (Style One)	315.00	360.00	180.00

Julie
Style Two

Designer: Elizabeth Greenshields
Modeller: Martin Evans
Height: 8", 20.3 cm
Colour: Purple
Issued: 1995 to the present
Varieties: Also called Hazel
Series: Ladies of Fashion

Name	U.S. $	Can. $	U.K. £
Julie (Style Two)	235.00	275.00	110.00

Juliette
Style One

Designer: Unknown
Height: Unknown
Colour: Unknown
Issued: 1982 - 1983
Series: Little Women

Name	U.S. $	Can. $	U.K. £
Juliette (Style One)	195.00	220.00	110.00

Photograph not available at press time

Juliette
Style Two

Designer: John Bromley
Modeller: John Bromley
Height: 5", 12.5 cm
Colour: White and blue dress
Issued: 1982 - 1985
Varieties: Also called Annette (Style Four); Claudette (Style Two); Jeanette (Style Two); Joanne (Style One); Lynette (StyleTwo) Sally Anne (Style One)
Series: Debutante Collection

Name	U.S. $	Can. $	U.K. £
Juliette (Style Two)	160.00	180.00	90.00

Juliette
Style Three

Designer: Helen Buckley
Modeller: Andy Moss
Height: 5 ½", 14.0 cm
Colour: Pale turquoise (porcelain)
Issued: 1997 - 1997
Series: Beau Monde Figure of the Year

Name	U.S. $	Can. $	U.K. £
Juliette (Style Three)	100.00	175.00	55.00

Julius Caesar

Designer: Robert Worthington
Height: 10 ½", 26.7 cm
Colour: White and red
Issued: 1981 in a limited edition of 2,000
Series: Characters from Shakespeare

Name	U.S. $	Can. $	U.K. £
Julius Caesar	450.00	525.00	265.00

June
Style Two

Designer: John Bromley
Modeller: John Bromley
Height: 5", 12.7 cm
Colour: Pale blue dress with flowered border
Issued: 1983 - 1989
Varieties: Also called Justine; Natalie (Style One); Samantha; Sophie (Style One); Tessa
Series: Debutante Collection

Name	U.S. $	Can. $	U.K. £
June (Style Two)	130.00	150.00	75.00

June
Style Three

Designer: John Bromley
Modeller: John Bromley
Height: 5", 12.7 cm
Colour: Unknown
Issued: 1987
Varieties: Also called Danielle (Style Two); Giselle (Style Two); Karen (Style One); Michelle (Style Two)
Series: Debutante Collection

Name	U.S. $	Can. $	U.K. £
June (Style Three)	165.00	190.00	95.00

Note: Commissioned by Grattan Home Shopping.

Just William

Designer: Catherine Barnsley
Height: Unknown
Colour: Blue
Issued: 1977 - c.1980
Series: Just William

Name	U.S. $	Can. $	U.K. £
Just William	300.00	350.00	175.00

Justine

Designer: John Bromley
Modeller: John Bromley
Height: 5", 12.7 cm
Colour: Pale green dress
Issued: 1983 - 1988
Varieties: Also called June; Natalie (Style One); Samantha (Style One); Sophie (Style One); Tessa
Series: Debutante Collection

Name	U.S. $	Can. $	U.K. £
Justine	150.00	170.00	85.00

Karen
Style One

Designer: John Bromley
Modeller: John Bromley
Height: 5", 12.7 cm
Colour: Lilac dress and hat with flowered border
Issued: 1983 - 1986
Varieties: Also called Danielle (Style Two); Giselle (Style Two); June (Style Three); Michelle (Style Two)
Series: Debutante Collection

Name	U.S. $	Can. $	U.K. £
Karen (Style One)	165.00	190.00	95.00

Karen
Style Two

Designer: Helen Buckley
Modeller: Jack Glynn
Height: 8", 20.3 cm
Colour: Yellow and peach
Issued: 1996 - 1996
Series: Figurine of the Year

Name	U.S. $	Can. $	U.K. £
Karen (Style Two)	250.00	295.00	150.00

Karen Kain as Snow Queen

Designer: John Bromley
Height: 9 ¾", 24.5 cm
Colour: White with gold design
Issued: 1986 in a limited edition of 500

Name	U.S. $	Can. $	U.K. £
Karen Kain as Snow Queen	300.00	400.00	200.00

Note: Issued in conjunction with the Canadian Kidney Foundation. Original issue price $295.00.

Kate
Style One

Designer: John Bromley
Modeller: John Bromley
Height: 8 ½", 21.6 cm
Colour: Red and white
Issued: 1976 - 1982
Varieties: Also called Christabel (Style One); Rachel (Style One)
Series: Ladies of Fashion

Name	U.S. $	Can. $	U.K.£
Kate (Style One)	325.00	375.00	185.00

Kate
Style Two

Designer: Elizabeth Greenshields
Modeller: Martin Evans
Height: 4 ¾", 12.1 cm
Colour: Pale yellow and beige (porcelain)
Issued: 1993 to the present
Series: Beau Monde

Name	U.S. $	Can. $	U.K. £
Kate (Style Two)	100.00	175.00	57.50

Katherine
Style One

Designer: John Bromley
Modeller: John Bromley
Height: 7 ¾", 19.5 cm
Colour: White floral dress with peach and green flowers
Issued: Unknown
Varieties: Also called Maureen; Rapture; Rosalee; Spring Song
Series: Ladies of Fashion

Name	U.S. $	Can. $	U.K. £
Katherine (Style One)	250.00	290.00	145.00

Katherine
Style Two

Designer: Elizabeth Greenshields
Modeller: Martin Evans
Height: 5 ¼", 13.3 cm
Colour: Blue (porcelain)
Issued: 1993 - 1994
Series: Beau Monde

Name	U.S. $	Can. $	U.K. £
Katherine (Style Two)	195.00	235.00	110.00

Katherine Howard

Designer: Unknown
Modeller: Robert Worthington
Height: 8", 20.3 cm
Colour: Green and beige
Issued: 1979 - 1992
Series: Royal Collection

Name	U.S. $	Can. $	U.K. £
Katherine Howard	550.00	650.00	325.00

Kathleen

Designer: John Bromley
Modeller: John Bromley
Height: 8 ¼", 21.0 cm
Colour: Turquoise
Issued: 1994 to the present
Varieties: Also called Wakefield Rose
Series: Ladies of Fashion

Name	U.S. $	Can. $	U.K. £
Kathleen	300.00	425.00	135.00

Katie

Designer: John Bromley
Modeller: John Bromley
Height: 5", 12.7 cm
Colour: Peach and white
Issued: 1990 - 1993
Series: Debutante Collection

Name	U.S. $	Can. $	U.K. £
Katie	140.00	160.00	80.00

Kay

Designer: Graham Miller
Modeller: Unknown
Height: 10", 25.4 cm
Colour: Pink
Issued: 1997 to the present
Varieties: Also called Susannah
Series: Silhouettes

Name	U.S. $	Can. $	U.K. £
Kay	115.00	235.00	72.50

Kelly

Designer:	John Bromley
Modeller:	John Bromley
Height:	6 ½", 16.5 cm
Colour:	Green dress with white flowered bodice
Issued:	1984 - 1988
Varieties:	Also called Tina
Series:	Ladies of Fashion

Name	U.S. $	Can. $	U.K. £
Kelly	300.00	350.00	175.00

Kerry

Designer:	Helen Buckley
Modeller:	John Bromley
Height:	5 ¼", 13.3 cm
Colour:	Yellow dress with flowers
Issued:	1987 - 1994
Varieties:	Also called Loretta; Meryl
Series:	Debutante Collection

Name	U.S. $	Can. $	U.K. £
Kerry	115.00	150.00	65.00

Kimberley
Style One

Designer:	John Bromley
Modeller:	John Bromley
Height:	5", 12.7 cm
Colour:	Rose-pink flowered dress with pale pink underskirt
Issued:	1984 - 1990
Varieties:	Also called Lydia (Style One); Veronica (Style One)
Series:	Debutante Collection

Name	U.S. $	Can. $	U.K. £
Kimberley (Style One)	125.00	140.00	70.00

Kimberley
Style Two

Designer:	Unknown
Modeller:	Martin Evans
Height:	3 ¾", 9.5 cm
Colour:	Pale pink
Issued:	1995 to the present
Varieties:	Also called Natalie (Style Two)
Series:	Minuettes

Name	U.S. $	Can. $	U.K. £
Kimberley (Style Two)	50.00	69.50	30.00

Kirsty
Style One

Designer:	John Bromley
Modeller:	John Bromley
Height:	3 ¼", 8.3 cm
Colour:	White and black
Issued:	1985 - 1988
Varieties:	Also called Zoe (Style One)
Series:	Kensington Collection

Name	U.S. $	Can. $	U.K. £
Kirsty (Style One)	85.00	100.00	50.00

Kirsty
Style Two

Designer:	Elizabeth Greenshields
Modeller:	Andy Moss
Height:	5", 12.7 cm
Colour:	Turquoise
Issued:	1997 to the present
Series:	Debutante Collection

Name	U.S. $	Can. $	U.K. £
Kirsty (Style Two)	90.00	155.00	52.50

Kitty
Style Two

Designer: Andrea Cox
Modeller: Jack Glynn
Height: 12", 30.5 cm
Colour: Purple and lilac dress
Issued: 1996 to the present
Series: The Roaring Twenties (Style Two)

Name	U.S. $	Can. $	U.K. £
Kitty (Style Two)	400.00	550.00	140.00

La Belle Creole

Designer: John Bromley
Modeller: John Bromley
Height: 8 ¾", 22.2 cm
Colour: Dark blue
Issued: 1976 - 1982
Series: Ladies of Fashion

Name	U.S. $	Can. $	U.K. £
La Belle Creole	285.00	325.00	165.00

L.A. Gala

Designer: David Shilling
Modeller: John Bromley
Height: 9", 22.9 cm
Colour: Lemon and lilac
Issued: 1988 in a limited edition of 1,000
Series: Designer Series

Name	U.S. $	Can. $	U.K. £
L.A. Gala	475.00	550.00	275.00

Lace

Designer:	Elizabeth Greenshields
Modeller:	John Bromley
Height:	7 ¼", 18.4 cm
Colour:	Blue
Issued:	1993 - 1993
Varieties:	Also called Dignity; High Style
Series:	Chantilly Lace

Name	U.S. $	Can. $	U.K. £
Lace	325.00	375.00	185.00

Ladies Day (on wooden plinth)

Designer:	John Bromley
Height:	8 ½", 21.6 cm
Colour:	Grey-blue
Issued:	1984 - 1987
Series:	Sporting Collection

Name	U.S. $	Can. $	U.K. £
Ladies Day	340.00	400.00	195.00

Lady Alice of the Royal Garden Party

Designer:	John Bromley
Height:	8 ¼", 21.0 cm
Colour:	White and pale pink dress and parasol; gold trimmings
Issued:	1992 in a limited edition of 12,500
Series:	La Belle Epoque

Name	U.S. $	Can. $	U.K. £
Lady Alice of the Royal Garden Party	265.00	300.00	150.00

Note: Commissioned by Compton and Woodhouse.

Lady Beatrice

Designer:	Richard Ellis
Height:	5 ½", 14.0 cm
Colour:	Green dress with darker green trim; gold walking cane
Issued:	1993
Series:	Royal Ascot Miniature Collection

Name	U.S. $	Can. $	U.K. £
Lady Beatrice	125.00	150.00	70.00

Note: Commissioned by Compton and Woodhouse.

Lady Caroline at the Summer Garden Party

Designer:	John Bromley
Height:	9 ½", 24.0 cm
Colour:	Pale pink and white dress; red sash and bows; gold trimmings
Issued:	1996 in a limited edition of 9,500
Series:	Edwardian Garden Party

Name	U.S. $	Can. $	U.K. £
Lady Caroline at the Summer Garden Party	300.00	350.00	175.00

Note: Commissioned by Compton and Woodhouse.

Lady Castlemaine

Designer:	Raymond Hughes
Modeller:	John Bromley
Height:	8 ¼", 21.0 cm
Colour:	Deep rose and white dress, gold trimmings; rose and gold fan
Issued:	1995 in a limited edition of 12,500
Series:	Femmes Fatales

Name	U.S. $	Can. $	U.K. £
Lady Castlemaine	280.00	325.00	160.00

Note: Commissioned by Compton and Woodhouse.

Lady Catherine

Designer: Richard Ellis
Height: 5 ½", 14.0 cm
Colour: Pale blue dress with deeper blue trim; white underskirt, shawl and hat
Issued: 1994
Series: Royal Ascot Miniature Collection

Name	U.S. $	Can. $	U.K. £
Lady Catherine	125.00	140.00	70.00

Note: Commissioned by Compton and Woodhouse.

Lady Clara

Designer: Richard Ellis
Height: 5 ½", 14.0 cm
Colour: Lilac dress and hat
Issued: 1994
Series: Royal Ascot Miniature Collection

Name	U.S. $	Can. $	U.K. £
Lady Clara	125.00	140.00	70.00

Note: Commissioned by Compton and Woodhouse.

Lady Diana Spencer

Designer: John Bromley
Height: 8 ½", 21.6 cm
Colour: Blue and white
Issued: 1981 in a limited edition of 1,000
Series: Royalty

Name	U.S. $	Can. $	U.K. £
Lady Diana Spencer	525.00	600.00	300.00

Lady Eliza

Designer: Richard Ellis
Height: 5 ½", 24.0 cm
Colour: Yellow and white dress trimmed with black; black hat with white feather and pink bow; white parasol
Issued: 1992
Series: Royal Ascot Miniature Collection

Name	U.S. $	Can. $	U.K. £
Lady Eliza	125.00	140.00	70.00

Note: Commissioned by Compton and Woodhouse.

Lady Emily

Designer: Richard Ellis
Height: 5 ½", 24.0 cm
Colour: Rust jacket; white blouse; cream skirt with green ribbon; rust and cream hat; gold highlights
Issued: 1993
Series: Royal Ascot Miniature Collection

Name	U.S. $	Can. $	U.K. £
Lady Emily	125.00	140.00	70.00

Note: Commissioned by Compton and Woodhouse.

Lady Emma

Designer: Richard Ellis
Height: 5 ½", 24.0 cm
Colour: Pink and white dress
Issued: 1993
Series: Royal Ascot Miniature Collection

Name	U.S. $	Can. $	U.K. £
Lady Emma	125.00	140.00	70.00

Note: Commissioned by Compton and Woodhouse.

Lady Evelyn

Designer: Richard Ellis
Height: 5 ½", 14.0 cm
Colour: Pink and white dress; grey shawl; pink hat with white feather
Issued: 1994
Series: Royal Ascot Miniature Collection

Name	U.S. $	Can. $	U.K. £
Lady Evelyn	125.00	140.00	70.00

Note: Commissioned by Compton and Woodhouse.

Lady Evelyn at the Country House Party

Designer: Jack Glynn
Height: 9", 22.9 cm
Colour: Pale pink and white dress and hat with red roses; gold trimmings
Issued: 1994 in a limited edition of 12,500
Series: La Belle Epoque

Name	U.S. $	Can. $	U.K. £
Lady Evelyn at the Country House Party	280.00	325.00	160.00

Note: Commissioned by Compton and Woodhouse.

Lady Florence

Designer: Richard Ellis
Height: 5 ½", 24.0 cm
Colour: Pink and white dress and hat
Issued: 1994
Series: Royal Ascot Miniature Collection

Name	U.S. $	Can. $	U.K. £
Lady Florence	125.00	140.00	70.00

Note: Commissioned by Compton and Woodhouse.

Lady Frances

Designer:	Richard Ellis
Height:	5 ½", 24.0 cm
Colour:	White dress with black trim; black hat with white feather
Issued:	1992
Series:	Royal Ascot Miniature Collection

Name	U.S. $	Can. $	U.K. £
Lady Frances	125.00	140.00	70.00

Note: Commissioned by Compton and Woodhouse.

Lady Frances on the Grand Tour

Designer:	John Bromley
Height:	9", 22.9 cm
Colour:	Pale pink and blue dress; pink hat with blue bow; white and blue parasol; gold trimmings
Issued:	1995 in a limited edition of 12,500
Series:	La Belle Epoque

Name	U.S. $	Can. $	U.K. £
Lady Frances on the Grand Tour	280.00	325.00	160.00

Note: Commissioned by Compton and Woodhouse.

Lady Grace

Designer:	Richard Ellis
Height:	5 ½", 24.0 cm
Colour:	Mauve and navy dress; white hat with navy bow
Issued:	1992
Series:	Royal Ascot Miniature Collection

Name	U.S. $	Can. $	U.K. £
Lady Grace	125.00	140.00	70.00

Note: Commissioned by Compton and Woodhouse.

Lady Harriet, The Royal Skating Party

Designer:	Jack Glynn
Height:	8 ½", 21.6 cm
Colour:	Peach overcoat; cream dress with peach and mauve design; gold trimming on coat, dress and hat
Issued:	1993 in a limited edition of 12,500
Series:	La Belle Epoque

Name	U.S. $	Can. $	U.K. £
Lady Harriet, The Royal Skating Party	280.00	325.00	160.00

Note: Commissioned by Compton and Woodhouse.

Lady Helena

Designer:	Richard Ellis
Height:	5 ½", 14.0 cm
Colour:	Aquamarine, white and navy dress; aquamarine hat with navy ribbon; brown dog
Issued:	1993
Series:	Royal Ascot Miniature Collection

Name	U.S. $	Can. $	U.K. £
Lady Helena	125.00	140.00	70.00

Note: Commissioned by Compton and Woodhouse.

Lady Helena Riding in Hyde Park

Designer:	Jack Glynn
Height:	8 ¼", 21.0 cm
Colour:	Cream riding habit with white underskirt; nutmeg waistcoat with gold trimming; gold riding crop
Issued:	1992 in a limited edition of 12,500
Series:	La Belle Epoque

Name	U.S. $	Can. $	U.K. £
Lady Helena Riding in Hyde Park	280.00	325.00	160.00

Note: Commissioned by Compton and Woodhouse.

Lady in Lace

Designer: Helen Buckley
Modeller: John Bromley
Height: 7 ¼", 18.4 cm
Colour: Pink and yellow
Issued: 1991 to the present
Varieties: Also called Rosemary (Style Two)
Series: Ladies of Fashion

Name	U.S. $	Can. $	U.K. £
Lady in Lace	300.00	485.00	150.00

Lady Lilian

Designer: Richard Ellis
Height: 5 ½", 14.0 cm
Colour: Rose-pink dress and hat; feather boa
Issued: 1992
Series: Royal Ascot Miniature Collection

Name	U.S. $	Can. $	U.K. £
Lady Lilian	125.00	140.00	70.00

Note: Commissioned by Compton and Woodhouse.

Lady Louise

Designer: Richard Ellis
Height: 5 ½", 14.0 cm
Colour: Pale grey and white dress; black hat with red roses; black gloves; pink and white parasol trimmed with black
Issued: 1993
Series: Royal Ascot Miniature Collection

Name	U.S. $	Can. $	U.K. £
Lady Louise	125.00	140.00	70.00

Note: Commissioned by Compton and Woodhouse.

Lady Lydia

Designer: Richard Ellis
Height: 5 ½", 14.0 cm
Colour: Pink dress with deeper pink flowers and ribbon; pink hat and parasol
Issued: 1994
Series: Royal Ascot Miniature Collection

Name	U.S. $	Can. $	U.K. £
Lady Lydia	125.00	140.00	70.00

Note: Commissioned by Compton and Woodhouse.

Lady May

Designer: Richard Ellis
Height: 5 ½", 14.0 cm
Colour: Yellow dress with lilac neckline, gold bows and waistband; yellow hat with red roses
Issued: 1994
Series: Royal Ascot Miniature Collection

Name	U.S. $	Can. $	U.K. £
Lady May	125.00	140.00	70.00

Note: Commissioned by Compton and Woodhouse.

Lady Phoebe

Designer: Richard Ellis
Height: 5 ½", 14.0 cm
Colour: Pale blue dress with pink and blue flowers; pale blue hat with deeper blue ribbon
Issued: 1993
Series: Royal Ascot Miniature Collection

Name	U.S. $	Can. $	U.K. £
Lady Phoebe	125.00	140.00	70.00

Note: Commissioned by Compton and Woodhouse.

Lady Rose
Style Two

Designer:	Richard Ellis
Height:	5 ½", 14.0 cm
Colour:	Lilac and white dress; white hat with lilac ribbons; white shawl
Issued:	1992
Series:	Royal Ascot Miniature Collection

Name	U.S. $	Can. $	U.K. £
Lady Rose (Style Two)	125.00	140.00	70.00

Note: Commissioned by Compton and Woodhouse.

Lady Rose at the Royal Ascot Ball

Designer:	Maureen Halson
Height:	8 ¼", 21.0 cm
Colour:	Pale pink dress; red rose on bodice; gold trimmings
Issued:	1993 in a limited edition of 12,500
Series:	La Belle Epoque

Name	U.S. $	Can. $	U.K. £
Lady Rose at the Royal Ascot Ball	280.00	325.00	160.00

Note: Commissioned by Compton and Woodhouse.

Lady Sara

Designer:	Helen Buckley
Modeller:	Jack Glynn
Height:	8 ½", 21.6 cm
Colour:	Blue and yellow
Issued:	1997 in a limited edition of 5,000
Series:	High Society

Name	U.S. $	Can. $	U.K. £
Lady Sara	400.00	595.00	200.00

Lady Sarah

Designer:	Richard Ellis
Height:	5 ½", 14.0 cm
Colour:	Cream dress and jade bolero; cream hat with white feather
Issued:	1992
Series:	Royal Ascot Miniature Collection

Name	U.S. $	Can. $	U.K. £
Lady Sarah	125.00	140.00	70.00

Note: Commissioned by Compton and Woodhouse.

Lady Sylvia

Designer:	John Bromley
Modeller:	John Bromley
Height:	10", 25.4 cm
Colour:	Pink and apricot with gold highlights
Issued:	1997 in a limited edition of 1,000
Series:	English Rose

Name	U.S. $	Can. $	U.K. £
Lady Sylvia	400.00	595.00	195.00

Lady with Dog, c.1810

Designer:	Mary Roberts
Modeller:	John Bromley
Height:	Unknown
Colour:	Yellow
Issued:	1985 in a limited edition of 500
Series:	Early Days

Name	U.S. $	Can. $	U.K. £
Lady with Dog, c.1810	395.00	450.00	225.00

Note: Commissioned for the Australian market.

Laetitia

Designer:	Elizabeth Greenshieldss
Modeller:	Martin Evans
Height:	5 ¼", 13.3 cm
Colour:	Pink and green (porcelain)
Issued:	1992 - 1994
Series:	Beau Monde

Name	U.S. $	Can. $	U.K. £
Laetitia	175.00	235.00	110.00

Landgirl

Designer:	John Bromley
Height:	8 ¼", 21.0 cm
Colour:	Green and brown
Issued:	1984 in a limited edition of 1,500
Series:	King and Country (1940 Period)

Name	U.S. $	Can. $	U.K. £
Landgirl	450.00	395.00	225.00

Laura
Style One

Designer:	John Bromley
Modeller:	John Bromley
Height:	7 ½", 19.1 cm
Colour:	Gold and white
Issued:	1984 - 1987
Series:	Ladies of Fashion

Name	U.S. $	Can. $	U.K. £
Laura (Style One)	285.00	325.00	165.00

Laura
Style Two

Designer: Elizabeth Greenshieldss
Modeller: Martin Evans
Height: 5 ½", 14.0 cm
Colour: Lavender (porcelain)
Issued: 1993 to the present
Series: Beau Monde

Name	U.S. $	Can. $	U.K. £
Laura (Style Two)	100.00	195.00	57.50

Photograph not available at press time

Laura Secord

Designer: John Bromley
Height: Unknown
Colour: Unknown
Issued: 1981

Name	U.S. $	Can. $	U.K. £
Laura Secord	150.00	190.00	95.00

Note: Commissioned by Home Canadian Collectibles, Unionville, Canada.

Lauren
Style One

Designer: John Bromley
Modeller: John Bromley
Height: 8 ½", 21.6 cm
Colour: White and gold
Issued: 1991 - 1993
Varieties: Also called High Society
Series: Grosvenor Collection

Name	U.S. $	Can. $	U.K. £
Lauren (Style One)	285.00	325.00	165.00

Lauren
Style Two

Designer: Elizabeth Greenshieldss
Modeller: Jack Glynn
Height: 4 ¾", 12.1 cm
Colour: Lemon and peach
Issued: 1995 to the present
Series: Debutante Collection

Name	U.S. $	Can. $	U.K. £
Lauren (Style Two)	100.00	150.00	52.50

Laurie Ann

Designer: John Bromley
Modeller: John Bromley
Height: 3 ¼", 8.3 cm
Colour: Purple
Issued: 1985 - 1988
Varieties: Also called Lesley (Style One)
Series: Kensington Collection

Name	U.S. $	Can. $	U.K. £
Laurie Ann	85.00	100.00	50.00

Lavender Seller (The)

Designer: John Bromley
Height: 8 ½", 21.6 cm
Colour: Lavender and white dress with pink flowers
Issued: 1993 in a limited edition of 9,500
Series: Cries of London

Name	U.S. $	Can. $	U.K. £
Lavender Seller (The)	280.00	325.00	160.00

Note: Commissioned by Compton and Woodhouse.

Lavender Walk

Designer: Elizabeth Greenshieldss
Modeller: Martin Evans
Height: 8 ¼", 21.0 cm
Colour: Lavender (porcelain)
Issued: 1994 - 1997
Varieties: Also called Megan
Series: Age of Elegance

Name	U.S. $	Can. $	U.K. £
Lavender Walk	250.00	325.00	125.00

Leanne

Designer: Unknown
Modeller: Martin Evans
Height: 3 ¾", 9.5 cm
Colour: Yellow and lemon
Issued: 1996 to the present
Varieties: Also called Grace (Style Three)
Series: Minuettes

Name	U.S. $	Can. $	U.K. £
Leanne	60.00	99.50	30.00

Leeds Centenary Ball

Designer: Unknown
Modeller: John Bromley
Height: 7 ¼", 18.5 cm
Colour: Sea-green
Issued: 1993 in a limited edition of 100
Series: Ladies of Fashion

Name	U.S. $	Can. $	U.K. £
Leeds Centenary Ball	775.00	900.00	450.00

Note: Commissioned by Peter Jones China Ltd., Wakefield.

Leona

Designer:	John Bromley
Height:	8", 20.3 cm
Colour:	Unknown
Issued:	1993 to the present
Varieties:	Also called Anthea (Style Two); Louisa
Series:	Ladies of Fashion

Name	U.S. $	Can. $	U.K. £
Leona	250.00	375.00	140.00

Note: Commissioned for the Australian market.

Lesley
Style One

Designer:	John Bromley
Modeller:	John Bromley
Height:	3 ¼", 8.3 cm
Colour:	White with gold trim
Issued:	1985 - 1988
Varieties:	Also called Laurie Ann
Series:	Kensington Collection

Name	U.S. $	Can. $	U.K. £
Lesley (Style One)	85.00	100.00	50.00

Lesley
Style Two

Designer:	Elizabeth Greenshields
Modeller:	Jack Glynn
Height:	5 ¼", 13.3 cm
Colour:	Peach
Issued:	1994 - 1996
Series:	Debutante Collection

Name	U.S. $	Can. $	U.K. £
Lesley (Style Two)	100.00	150.00	65.00

Letter (The)

Designer: Val Littlewood
Modeller: Jack Glynn
Height: 10 ½", 26.7 cm
Colour: Pink, cream, pale green and gold
Issued: 1997 in a limited edition of 250

Name	U.S. $	Can. $	U.K. £
Letter (The)	1,500.00	2,300.00	875.00

Letter From a Lover

Designer: John Bromley
Modeller: John Bromley
Height: 8", 20.3 cm
Colour: Gold and brown
Issued: 1977 - 1982
Series: Ladies of Fashion

Name	U.S. $	Can. $	U.K. £
Letter From a Lover	285.00	325.00	165.00

Lilac Time

Designer: Jack Glynn
Height: 9", 22.9 cm
Colour: Lilac gown and hat with lilac and pink flowers; basket of lilacs rests on a pedestal; gold trimmings
Issued: 1996 in a limited edition of 7,500
Series: Celebration of the Seasons

Name	U.S. $	Can. $	U.K. £
Lilac Time	280.00	320.00	160.00

Note: Commissioned by Compton and Woodhouse.

Lillie Langtry

Designer:	Raymond Hughes
Modeller:	John Bromley
Height:	8 ¼", 21.0 cm
Colour:	White dress with pink roses and lace trim; gold design on bodice; white fan with gold highlights
Issued:	1991 in a limited edition of 12,500
Series:	Femmes Fatales

Name	U.S. $	Can. $	U.K. £
Lillie Langtry	280.00	320.00	160.00

Note: Commissioned by Compton and Woodhouse.

Lily
Style One

Designer:	Elizabeth Greenshields
Modeller:	Unknown
Height:	8", 20.3 cm
Colour:	Blue
Issued:	1993 - 1993
Series:	Figurine of the Year

Name	U.S. $	Can. $	U.K. £
Lily (Style One)	425.00	500.00	250.00

Lily
Style Two

Designer:	Jack Glynn
Height:	9", 22.9 cm
Colour:	Pale yellow crinoline gown; basket of lilies
Issued:	1994 in a limited edition of 12,500
Series:	The Four Flowers Collection

Name	U.S. $	Can. $	U.K. £
Lily (Style Two)	280.00	325.00	160.00

Note: Commissioned by Compton and Woodhouse.

Lily
Style Three

Designer: Jack Glynn
Height: 3 ½", 8.9 cm
Colour: Orange overdress; pale peach underskirt with orange lilies; gold highlights
Issued: 1993 in a limited edition of 15,000
Series: Fairest Flowers

Name	U.S. $	Can. $	U.K. £
Lily (Style Three)	100.00	140.00	69.99

Note: Commissioned by Compton and Woodhouse.

Photograph not available at press time

Lily
Style Four

Designer: Maureen Halson
Height: Unknown
Colour: Lilac dress; bouquet and headdress of lilies; gold jewellery
Issued: 1995 in a limited edition of 4,500
Series: Flowers of Love

Name	U.S. $	Can. $	U.K. £
Lily (Style Four)	280.00	325.00	160.00

Note: Commissioned by Compton and Woodhouse.

Linda
Style One

Designer: John Bromley
Modeller: John Bromley
Height: 8", 20.3 cm
Colour: Yellow
Issued: 1977 - 1988
Varieties: Also called Debbie; Gillian (Style One); Melody; Philippa (Style One)
Series: Ladies of Fashion

Name	U.S. $	Can. $	U.K. £
Linda (Style One)	250.00	290.00	145.00

Linda
Style Two

Designer: Helen Buckley
Modeller: Jack Glynn
Height: 6 ½", 16.5 cm
Colour: Blue
Issued: 1997 to the present
Series: Ladies of Fashion

Name	U.S. $	Can. $	U.K. £
Linda (Style Two)	150.00	295.00	110.00

Lindsay

Designer: John Bromley
Modeller: John Bromley
Height: 5", 12.7 cm
Colour: Rust
Issued: 1986 - 1989
Varieties: Also called Dee; Zara
Series: Debutante Collection

Name	U.S. $	Can. $	U.K. £
Lindsay	130.00	150.00	75.00

Lindsey

Designer: Helen Buckley
Modeller: Martin Evans
Height: 7 ¾", 19.7 cm
Colour: Blue
Issued: 1997 to the present
Varieties: Also called Jean (Style Two)
Series: Ladies of Fashion

Name	U.S. $	Can. $	U.K. £
Lindsey	175.00	200.00	99.95

Note: Commissioned by Grattan Home Shopping.

Lisa
Style One

Designer: John Bromley
Modeller: John Bromley
Height: 6 ½", 16.5 cm
Colour: Pale blue
Issued: 1977 - 1982
Varieties: Also called Elizabeth (Style One); Polly
Series: Ladies of Fashion

Name	U.S. $	Can. $	U.K. £
Lisa (Style One)	300.00	350.00	175.00

Lisa
Style Two

Designer: John Bromley
Modeller: John Bromley
Height: 5", 12.7 cm
Colour: Blue and green
Issued: 1993 - 1996
Varieties: Also called Selina (Style Two)
Series: Debutante Collection

Name	U.S. $	Can. $	U.K. £
Lisa (Style Two)	125.00	150.00	55.00

Little Swan

Designer: David Lyttleton
Height: 7 ½", 19.1 cm
Colour: White
Issued: 1992 in a limited edition of 9,500
Series: The Ballet Shoes Collection

Name	U.S. $	Can. $	U.K. £
Little Swan	140.00	160.00	80.00

Photograph not available at press time

Little Workman (The)

Designer: John Bromley
Modeller: John Bromley
Height: 4 ¾", 11.5 cm
Colour: Blue dungarees and yellow sweater
Issued: 1980 - unknown
Series: Children Studies

Name	U.S. $	Can. $	U.K. £
Little Workman (The)	285.00	325.00	165.00

L'Ombrelle

Designer: John Bromley
Modeller: John Bromley
Height: 8 ¼", 21.0 cm
Colour: Pale blue dress; pink parasol
Issued: 1977 - 1985
Series: Ladies of Fashion

Name	U.S. $	Can. $	U.K. £
L'Ombrelle	300.00	350.00	175.00

Lord Nelson

Designer: Robert Worthington
Height: 9 ½", 24.0 cm
Colour: Navy, gold and beige
Issued: 1979 - unknown
Series: Historical Figures

Name	U.S. $	Can. $	U.K. £
Lord Nelson	395.00	450.00	225.00

Loretta

Designer:	Helen Buckley
Modeller:	John Bromley
Height:	5 ¼", 13.3 cm
Colour:	Lilac
Issued:	1987 to the present
Varieties:	Also called Kerry; Meryl
Series:	Debutante Collection

Name	U.S. $	Can. $	U.K. £
Loretta	95.00	160.00	52.50

Lorna

Designer:	John Bromley
Modeller:	John Bromley
Height:	4 ½", 11.9 cm
Colour:	Green and yellow
Issued:	1990 - 1992
Series:	Debutante Collection

Name	U.S. $	Can. $	U.K. £
Lorna	150.00	170.00	85.00

Lorraine

Designer:	John Bromley
Modeller:	John Bromley
Height:	7 ½", 19.1 cm
Colour:	White with gold trim
Issued:	1983 - 1991
Varieties:	Also called Stephanie (Style One)
Series:	Ladies of Fashion

Name	U.S. $	Can. $	U.K. £
Lorraine	285.00	325.00	165.00

Louisa

Designer: John Bromley
Height: 8", 20.3 cm
Colour: Peach
Issued: 1993 to the present
Varieties: Also called Anthea (Style Two); Leona
Series: Ladies of Fashion

Name	U.S. $	Can. $	U.K. £
Louisa	250.00	375.00	140.00

Louisa at Ascot

Designer: Shirley Curzon
Modeller: John Bromley
Height: 8 ½", 21.6 cm
Colour: White and lilac dress
Issued: 1987 in a limited edition of 12,500
Series: Golden Age

Name	U.S. $	Can. $	U.K. £
Louisa at Ascot	225.00	260.00	130.00

Note: Commissioned by Compton and Woodhouse.

Louise

Designer: John Bromley
Height: 7 ½", 19.1 cm
Colour: Blue and white
Issued: 1975 - 1977
Varieties: Also called Anne Marie; Julie (Style One)
Series: Ladies of Fashion

Name	U.S. $	Can. $	U.K. £
Louise	285.00	325.00	165.00

Love Token

Designer:	Unknown
Height:	5", 12.7 cm
Colour:	Turquoise
Issued:	1992 - 1995
Series:	Debutante Collection

Name	U.S. $	Can. $	U.K. £
Love Token	130.00	150.00	75.00

Lovely Lady Christabel (The)

Designer:	Basia Zarzycka
Modeller:	Martin Evans
Height:	8 ½", 21.6 cm
Colour:	Cream with silver highlights and flowers
Issued:	1997 to the present
Series:	Basia Zarzycka Collection

Name	U.S. $	Can. $	U.K. £
Lovely Lady Christabel (The)	400.00	595.00	195.00

Love's Dream

Designer:	John Bromley
Modeller:	John Bromley
Height:	8", 20.3 cm
Colour:	Green
Issued:	1984 - 1986
Varieties:	Also called First Dance; Melanie (Style One)
Series:	Ladies of Fashion

Name	U.S. $	Can. $	U.K. £
Love's Dream	300.00	350.00	175.00

Lucinda
Style One

Designer:	John Bromley
Height:	9", 22.9 cm
Colour:	Brown
Issued:	1985 - 1987
Series:	High Style Collection

Name	U.S. $	Can. $	U.K. £
Lucinda (Style One)	475.00	550.00	275.00

Lucinda
Style Two

Designer:	John Bromley
Modeller:	John Bromley
Height:	5", 12.7 cm
Colour:	Lavender
Issued:	1993 - 1995
Series:	Debutante Collection

Name	U.S. $	Can. $	U.K. £
Lucinda (Style Two)	130.00	150.00	65.00

Lucy
Style One

Designer:	John Bromley
Modeller:	John Bromley
Height:	8 ½", 21.6 cm
Colour:	Burgundy dress with peach underskirt
Issued:	1975 - 1979
Varieties:	Also called Annabelle (Style One); Sarah (Style One)
Series:	Ladies of Fashion

Name	U.S. $	Can. $	U.K. £
Lucy (Style One)	285.00	325.00	165.00

Lucy
Style Two

Designer: Pauline Shone
Height: Unknown
Colour: White
Issued: 1979 - unknown
Series: Children Studies

Name	U.S. $	Can. $	U.K. £
Lucy (Style Two)	250.00	290.00	145.00

Lucy
Style Three

Designer: John Bromley
Modeller: John Bromley
Height: 5", 12.7 cm
Colour: Pink
Issued: 1992 to the present
Series: Debutante Collection

Name	U.S. $	Can. $	U.K. £
Lucy	100.00	150.00	52.50

Lydia
Style One

Designer: John Bromley
Modeller: John Bromley
Height: 5", 12.7 cm
Colour: Peach
Issued: 1984 - 1988
Varieties: Also called Kimberley (Style One); Veronica (Style One)
Series: Debutante Collection

Name	U.S. $	Can. $	U.K. £
Lydia (Style One)	165.00	190.00	95.00

Lydia
Style Two

Designer:	Graham Miller
Modeller:	Unknown
Height:	10", 25.4 cm
Colour:	Pink
Issued:	1997 to the present
Varieties:	Also called Nicola
Series:	Silhouettes

Name	U.S. $	Can. $	U.K. £
Lydia (Style Two)	130.00	235.00	72.50

Lynette
Style One

Designer:	Unknown
Height:	Unknown
Colour:	Unknown
Issued:	1982 - 1983
Series:	Little Women

Name	U.S. $	Can. $	U.K. £
Lynette (Style One)	165.00	190.00	95.00

Photograph not available at press time

Lynette
Style Two

Designer:	John Bromley
Modeller:	John Bromley
Height:	5", 12.7 cm
Colour:	White and yellow dress with yellow flowers
Issued:	1982 - 1985
Varieties:	Also called Annette (Style Four); Claudette (Style Two); Jeanette (Style Two); Joanne (Style One); Juliette (Style Two); Sally Anne (Style One)
Series:	Debutante Collection

Name	U.S. $	Can. $	U.K. £
Lynette (Style Two)	165.00	190.00	95.00

Lynne
Style One

Designer: John Bromley
Modeller: John Bromley
Height: 8", 20.3 cm
Colour: Brown
Issued: 1980 - 1988
Varieties: Also called Tara
Series: Ladies of Fashion

Name	U.S. $	Can. $	U.K. £
Lynne (Style One)	285.00	325.00	165.00

Lynne
Style Two

Designer: Elizabeth Greenshields
Modeller: Martin Evans
Height: 5 ½", 14.0 cm
Colour: Pale blue dress with dark blue bows and white frills (porcelain)
Issued: 1994 to the present
Series: Beau Monde

Name	U.S. $	Can. $	U.K. £
Lynne (Style Two)	115.00	175.00	57.50

Madame de Pompadour

Designer: Raymond Hughes
Modeller: John Bromley
Height: 8 ¼", 21.0 cm
Colour: Pale pink gown; red rose; gold trimmings
Issued: 1994 in a limited edition of 12,500
Series: Femmes Fatales

Name	U.S. $	Can. $	U.K. £
Madame de Pompadour	280.00	325.00	158.00

Note: Commissioned by Compton and Woodhouse.

Madelaine

Designer:	Unknown
Modeller:	Martin Evans
Height:	4 ¾", 12.1 cm
Colour:	Pale blue, white and pink (porcelain)
Issued:	1996 to the present
Series:	Beau Monde

Name	U.S. $	Can. $	U.K. £
Madelaine	100.00	150.00	57.50

Madeline

Designer:	John Bromley
Modeller:	John Bromley
Height:	7", 17.8 cm
Colour:	Orange-red with gold trim
Issued:	1977 - 1988
Varieties:	Also called The Ball
Series:	Ladies of Fashion

Name	U.S. $	Can. $	U.K. £
Madeline	285.00	325.00	165.00

Mademoiselle Cherie

Designer:	Helen Buckley
Modeller:	Jack Glynn
Height:	10 ½", 26.7 cm
Colour:	Pink gown with blue bows
Issued:	1997 in a limited edition of 3,000
Series:	Les Parisiennes

Name	U.S. $	Can. $	U.K. £
Mademoiselle Cherie	450.00	575.00	225.00

Magnolia Parade

Designer: Helen Buckley
Modeller: Jack Glynn
Height: 8 ¼", 21.0 cm
Colour: Pale peach and blue (porcelain)
Issued: 1997 to the present
Series: Age of Elegance

Name	U.S. $	Can. $	U.K. £
Magnolia Parade	175.00	355.00	120.00

Making Up

Designer: Pauline Shone
Height: Unknown
Colour: White and pink
Issued: 1979 - unknown
Series: Children Studies

Name	U.S. $	Can. $	U.K. £
Making Up	250.00	290.00	145.00

Malvolio

Designer: Robert Worthington
Height: 10 ½", 26.7 cm
Colour: Brown
Issued: 1981 - 1982
Series: Characters from Shakespeare

Name	U.S. $	Can. $	U.K. £
Malvolio	475.00	550.00	275.00

Mandarin Crescent

Designer: Helen Buckley
Modeller: Jack Glynn
Height: 9", 22.9 cm
Colour: Blue (porcelain)
Issued: 1997 to the present
Series: Age of Elegance

Name	U.S. $	Can. $	U.K. £
Mandarin Crescent	225.00	355.00	140.00

Margaret
Style One

Designer: John Bromley
Modeller: John Bromley
Height: 8 ½", 21.6 cm
Colour: Red and blue
Issued: 1978 - 1989
Series: Ladies of Fashion

Name	U.S. $	Can. $	U.K. £
Margaret (Style One)	280.00	325.00	160.00

Margaret
Style Two

Designer: Helen Buckley
Modeller: Jack Glynn
Height: 8 ¼", 21.0 cm
Colour: Green and white
Issued: 1997 - 1997
Series: Special Events

Name	U.S. $	Can. $	U.K. £
Margaret (Style Two)	200.00	295.00	100.00

Maria

Designer: Elizabeth Greenshields
Modeller: John Bromley
Height: 8", 20.3 cm
Colour: Blue
Issued: 1992 - 1994
Series: Ladies of Fashion

Name	U.S. $	Can. $	U.K. £
Maria	285.00	325.00	165.00

Marianne

Designer: John Bromley
Modeller: John Bromley
Height: 7 ¾", 19.7 cm
Colour: Yellow
Issued: 1986 - 1990
Varieties: Also called Miranda
Series: Ladies of Fashion

Name	U.S. $	Can. $	U.K. £
Marianne	265.00	300.00	150.00

Marie
Style One

Designer: Helen Buckley
Modeller: John Bromley
Height: 8 ¼", 21.0 cm
Colour: Grey-blue dress
Issued: 1988 - 1989
Series: Brides

Name	U.S. $	Can. $	U.K. £
Marie (Style One)	300.00	350.00	175.00

Marie
Style Two

Designer: Martin Evans
Height: 5 ½", 14.0 cm
Colour: Yellow dress
Issued: 1996
Varieties: Also called Rose (Style Three)
Series: Debutante Collection

Name	U.S. $	Can. $	U.K. £
Marie (Style Two)	85.00	100.00	49.95

Note: Commissioned by Freemans Home Shopping.

Marie Antoinette

Designer: Raymond Hughes
Modeller: John Bromley
Height: 8 ¼", 21.0 cm
Colour: Turquoise gown trimmed with cream, pink and gold; gold flowered fan
Issued: 1992 in a limited edition of 12,500
Series: Femmes Fatales

Name	U.S. $	Can. $	U.K. £
Marie Antoinette	280.00	325.00	158.00

Note: Commissioned by Compton and Woodhouse.

Marilyn
Style One

Designer: John Bromley
Height: 8", 20.3 cm
Colour: Pink
Issued: 1980 - 1982
Series: Ladies of Fashion

Name	U.S. $	Can. $	U.K. £
Marilyn (Style One)	325.00	375.00	185.00

Marilyn
Style Two

Designer: Elizabeth Greenshields
Modeller: Unknown
Height: 8", 20.3 cm
Colour: Pink
Issued: 1992 - 1993
Series: West End Girls

Name	U.S. $	Can. $	U.K. £
Marilyn (Style Two)	285.00	325.00	165.00

Marjorie

Designer: John Bromley
Modeller: John Bromley
Height: 8 ½", 21.6 cm
Colour: Deep blue dress with flowers
Issued: 1987 - 1990
Varieties: Also called Antonia; Enchantress
Series: Ladies of Fashion

Name	U.S. $	Can. $	U.K. £
Marjorie	325.00	395.00	150.00

Mark Antony

Designer: Robert Worthington
Height: 10 ½", 26.7 cm
Colour: Red
Issued: 1981 - 1982
Series: Characters from Shakespeare

Name	U.S. $	Can. $	U.K. £
Mark Antony	475.00	550.00	275.00

Marlena

Designer: John Bromley
Modeller: John Bromley
Height: 9 ½", 24.0 cm
Colour: Peach
Issued: 1993 in a limited edition of 1,000
Series: English Rose

Name	U.S. $	Can. $	U.K. £
Marlena	425.00	500.00	250.00

Marlene

Designer: Helen Buckley
Modeller: John Bromley
Height: 8", 20.3 cm
Colour: Red and white
Issued: 1988 - 1990
Series: Ladies of Fashion

Name	U.S. $	Can. $	U.K. £
Marlene	285.00	325.00	165.00

Martha

Designer: Unknown
Modeller: John Bromley
Height: 7 ¾", 19.7 cm
Colour: Pink and white
Issued: 1979 - 1982
Series: Ladies of Fashion

Name	U.S. $	Can. $	U.K. £
Martha	325.00	375.00	185.00

Martha Rose

Designer: Elizabeth Greenshields
Modeller: Jack Glynn
Height: 7 ¼", 18.4 cm
Colour: Pink
Issued: 1995 in a limited edition
Varieties: Also called On the Balcony
Series: Age of Elegance

Name	U.S. $	Can. $	U.K. £
Martha Rose	225.00	260.00	130.00

Note: Commissioned by the Ironbridge Museum to commemorate the wife of the founder of the museum.

Mary
Style One

Designer: John Bromley
Modeller: John Bromley
Height: 5", 12.7 cm
Colour: Dark green
Issued: 1983 - 1990
Varieties: Also called Gwen; Jill (Style One); Tracy; Vivienne
Series: Debutante Collection

Name	U.S. $	Can. $	U.K. £
Mary (Style One)	130.00	150.00	75.00

Mary
Style Two

Designer: Helen Buckley
Modeller: Jack Glynn
Height: 6 ½", 16.5 cm
Colour: Rose-pink
Issued: 1996 - 1996
Series: Collingwood Collection (Membership exclusive)

Name	U.S. $	Can. $	U.K. £
Mary (Style Two)	225.00	250.00	200.00

Mary Tudor
(1516 - 1558)

Designer: Michael Abberley
Height: 8 ¼", 21.0 cm
Colour: Burgundy and grey
Issued: 1990 in a limited edition of 1,000
Series: Queens of England

Name	U.S. $	Can. $	U.K. £
Mary Tudor (1516-1558)	525.00	600.00	295.00

Match Point
(on wooden plinth)

Designer: John Bromley
Height: 8 ½", 21.6 cm
Colour: White and red (matte)
Issued: 1984 - 1987
Series: Sporting Collection

Name	U.S. $	Can. $	U.K. £
Match Point	395.00	450.00	225.00

Match Seller

Designer: Margaret Whittaker
Height: 7", 17.8 cm
Colour: Blue trousers, brown jacket and cap; black boots; brown tray of matches
Issued: 1977 - unknown
Series: Old London Streets

Name	U.S. $	Can. $	U.K. £
Match Seller	340.00	400.00	195.00

Matinee Performance

Designer:	John Bromley
Modeller:	John Bromley
Height:	8", 20.3 cm
Colour:	Lavender, black and purple (porcelain)
Issued:	1996 to the present
Varieties:	Also called White Rose of Yorkshire
Series:	Age of Elegance

Name	U.S. $	Can. $	U.K. £
Matinee Performance	250.00	325.00	115.00

Maureen

Designer:	John Bromley
Modeller:	John Bromley
Height:	8", 20.3 cm
Colour:	Blue dress with black highlights
Issued:	1980 - 1986
Varieties:	Also called Katherine (Style One); Rapture; Rosalee; Spring Song
Series:	Ladies of Fashion

Name	U.S. $	Can. $	U.K. £
Maureen	285.00	325.00	165.00

Maxine

Designer:	John Bromley
Modeller:	John Bromley
Height:	5", 12.7 cm
Colour:	Dark and pale blue
Issued:	1983 - 1986
Varieties:	Also called Andrea; Claire (Style One); Pamela (Style One); Susan (Style One)
Series:	Debutante Collection

Name	U.S. $	Can. $	U.K. £
Maxine	150.00	175.00	85.00

May

Designer: Jack Glynn
Height: 3 ½", 8.9 cm
Colour: Peach overdress; white underskirt with May blossom; gold trimming
Issued: 1993 in a limited edition of 15,000
Series: Fairest Flowers

Name	U.S. $	Can. $	U.K. £
May	125.00	140.00	70.00

Note: Commissioned by Compton and Woodhouse.

May Ball

Designer: Helen Buckley
Modeller: John Bromley
Height: 5", 12.7 cm
Colour: Yellow and pink
Issued: 1991 to the present
Varieties: Also called Garden Party (The)
Series: Debutante Collection

Name	U.S. $	Can. $	U.K. £
May Ball	100.00	160.00	52.50

May Queen

Designer: John Bromley
Modeller: John Bromley
Height: 9 ½", 24.0 cm
Colour: Pink
Issued: 1992 in a limited edition of 1,000
Series: English Rose

Name	U.S. $	Can. $	U.K. £
May Queen	550.00	650.00	325.00

Medicine Man (The)

Designer:	Robert Worthington
Height:	8", 20.3 cm
Colour:	Black suit and hat; blue waistcoat; brown medicine chest
Issued:	1982 - 1985
Series:	Character Collection

Name	U.S. $	Can. $	U.K. £
Medicine Man	340.00	400.00	195.00

Meeting at Ascot (A)

Designer:	Shirley Curzon
Modeller:	John Bromley
Height:	9", 22.9 cm
Colour:	Pale peach dress with darker peach highlights; beige hat with roses; peach parasol
Issued:	1997 in a limited edition of 9,500
Series:	Elegant Edwardians

Name	U.S. $	Can. $	U.K. £
Meeting at Ascot (A)	280.00	325.00	160.00

Note: Commissioned by Compton and Woodhouse.

Megan

Designer:	Elizabeth Greenshields
Modeller:	Martin Evans
Height:	8 ¼", 21.0 cm
Colour:	Rose-pink
Issued:	1997 in a limited edition of 250
Varieties:	Also called Lavender Walk
Series:	Welsh Ladies of Fashion

Name	U.S. $	Can. $	U.K. £
Megan	175.00	200.00	99.95

Note: Commissioned by J. T. Morgan, Swansea, Wales.

Melanie
Style One

Designer:	John Bromley
Modeller:	John Bromley
Height:	8", 20.3 cm
Colour:	White with blue trim
Issued:	1979 - 1989
Varieties:	Also called First Dance; Love's Dream
Series:	Ladies of Fashion

Name	U.S. $	Can. $	U.K. £
Melanie (Style One)	265.00	300.00	150.00

Melanie
Style Two

Designer:	Helen Buckley
Modeller:	Andy Moss
Height:	4", 10.1 cm
Colour:	Blue
Issued:	1997 to the present
Series:	Debutante Collection

Name	U.S. $	Can. $	U.K. £
Melanie (Style Two)	100.00	155.00	52.50

Melissa

Designer:	John Bromley
Modeller:	John Bromley
Height:	8 ½", 21.6 cm
Colour:	Green
Issued:	1984 - 1987
Varieties:	Also called Adele; Glenda
Series:	Ladies of Fashion

Name	U.S. $	Can. $	U.K. £
Melissa	265.00	300.00	175.00

Melody

Designer: John Bromley
Modeller: John Bromley
Height: 8", 20.3 cm
Colour: Pink
Issued: 1987 - 1991
Varieties: Also called Debbie; Gillian (Style One); Linda (Style One); Philippa (Style One)
Series: Ladies of Fashion

Name	U.S. $	Can. $	U.K. £
Melody	340.00	395.00	150.00

Meryl

Designer: John Bromley
Modeller: John Bromley
Height: 5 ¼", 13.3 cm
Colour: Brown and beige
Issued: 1987 - 1994
Varieties: Also called Kerry; Loretta
Series: Debutante Collection

Name	U.S. $	Can. $	U.K. £
Meryl	130.00	150.00	65.00

Michele

Designer: John Bromley
Modeller: John Bromley
Height: 8 ½", 21.6 cm
Colour: Green
Issued: 1976 - 1979
Varieties: Also called Charlotte (Style One); Patricia (Style One)
Series: Ladies of Fashion

Name	U.S. $	Can. $	U.K. £
Michele	325.00	375.00	185.00

Photograph not available at press time

Michelle
Style One

Designer: Unknown
Height: Unknown
Colour: Unknown
Issued: 1982 - 1983
Series: Little Women

Name	U.S. $	Can. $	U.K. £
Michelle (Style One)	165.00	190.00	95.00

Michelle
Style Two

Designer: John Bromley
Modeller: John Bromley
Height: 5", 12.7 cm
Colour: Peach
Issued: 1982 - 1986
Varieties: Also called Danielle (Style Two); Giselle (Style Two); June (Style Three); Karen (Style One)
Series: Debutante Collection

Name	U.S. $	Can. $	U.K. £
Michelle (Style Two)	165.00	190.00	95.00

Michelle
Style Three

Designer: Unknown
Modeller: Martin Evans
Height: 3 ½", 8.9 cm
Colour: Pink
Issued: 1995 to the present
Varieties: Also called Hannah (Style Two); Summertime
Series: Minuettes

Name	U.S. $	Can. $	U.K. £
Michelle (Style Three)	55.00	69.50	30.00

Midsummer Dream

Designer: Helen Buckley
Modeller: Jack Glynn
Height: 9", 22.9 cm
Colour: Yellow and peach (porcelain)
Issued: 1997 - 1997
Series: Age of Elegance Figure of the Year

Name	U.S. $	Can. $	U.K. £
Midsummer Dream	200.00	295.00	100.00

Midsummer Stroll

Designer: Elizabeth Greenshields
Modeller: Martin Evans
Height: 8 ¾", 22.2 cm
Colour: Green and peach (porcelain)
Issued: 1992 - 1997
Series: Age of Elegance

Name	U.S. $	Can. $	U.K. £
Midsummer Stroll	300.00	445.00	160.00

Mikado

Designer: Margaret Whittaker
Height: 8 ½", 21.6 cm
Colour: Brown and pink
Issued: 1979 - 1981
Series: Gilbert and Sullivan

Name	U.S. $	Can. $	U.K. £
Mikado	575.00	650.00	325.00

Milk Maid

Designer:	John Bromley
Height:	8 ½", 21.6 cm
Colour:	White, blue and peach
Issued:	1996 in a limited edition of 9,500
Series:	The Cries of London

Name	U.S. $	Can. $	U.K. £
Milk Maid	280.00	325.00	160.00

Note: Commissioned by Compton and Woodhouse.

Millie
Style One

Designer:	John Bromley
Modeller:	John Bromley
Height:	5", 12.7 cm
Colour:	Yellow
Issued:	1988 - 1990
Series:	Debutante Collection

Name	U.S. $	Can. $	U.K. £
Millie (Style One)	150.00	170.00	85.00

Millie
Style Two

Designer:	Andrea Cox
Modeller:	Jack Glynn
Height:	12", 30.5 cm
Colour:	Grey dress; red cloak with beige fur trim coat
Issued:	1997 to the present
Series:	The Roaring Twenties (Style Two)

Name	U.S. $	Can. $	U.K. £
Millie (Style Two)	300.00	550.00	140.00

Miranda

Designer: John Bromley
Modeller: John Bromley
Height: 7 ¾", 19.7 cm
Colour: Green
Issued: 1988 - 1990
Varieties: Also called Marianne
Series: Ladies of Fashion

Name	U.S. $	Can. $	U.K. £
Miranda	250.00	290.00	145.00

Mirinda

Designer: Elizabeth Greenshields
Modeller: Unknown
Height: 5 ¼", 13.3 cm
Colour: Green
Issued: 1993 - 1996
Series: Debutante Collection

Name	U.S. $	Can. $	U.K. £
Mirinda	125.00	160.00	65.00

Miss 1920

Designer: John Bromley
Height: 9", 22.9 cm
Colour: Blue coat and hat; pink pants; black boots;
white muff; coat, hat and boots trimmed with ermine
Issued: 1982 - 1985
Series: Vogue

Name	U.S. $	Can. $	U.K. £
Miss 1920	475.00	550.00	275.00

Miss 1921

Designer: John Bromley
Height: 8 ½", 21.5 cm
Colour: Green jacket, yellow skirt; yellow hat and shoes; brown dog
Issued: 1982 - 1986
Series: Vogue

Name	U.S. $	Can. $	U.K. £
Miss 1921	425.00	500.00	250.00

Miss 1922

Designer: John Bromley
Height: Unknown
Colour: Pink
Issued: 1983 - 1985
Series: Vogue

Name	U.S. $	Can. $	U.K. £
Miss 1922	425.00	500.00	250.00

Photograph not available at press time

Photograph not available at press time

Miss 1923

Designer: John Bromley
Height: Unknown
Colour: Unknown
Issued: 1983 - 1985
Series: Vogue

Name	U.S. $	Can. $	U.K. £
Miss 1923	475.00	550.00	275.00

Miss 1924

Designer: John Bromley
Height: Unknown
Colour: Pink coat with grey fur trim; blue trousers and shoes; blond hair
Issued: 1982 - 1985
Series: Vogue

Name	U.S. $	Can. $	U.K. £
Miss 1924	475.00	550.00	275.00

Miss 1925

Designer: John Bromley
Height: 8 ¼", 21.0 cm
Colour: Orange dress; white feather
Issued: 1981 - 1985
Series: Vogue

Name	U.S. $	Can. $	U.K. £
Miss 1925	425.00	500.00	250.00

Miss 1926

Designer: John Bromley
Height: 8 ¾", 22.2 cm
Colour: Pink coat; blue skirt; white top and hat
Issued: 1981 - 1985
Series: Vogue

Name	U.S. $	Can. $	U.K. £
Miss 1926	425.00	500.00	250.00

Photograph not available at press time

Miss 1927

Designer:	John Bromley
Height:	Unknown
Colour:	Unknown
Issued:	1983 - 1985
Series:	Vogue

Name	U.S. $	Can. $	U.K. £
Miss 1927	425.00	500.00	250.00

Miss 1928

Designer:	John Bromley
Height:	8 ½", 21.6 cm
Colour:	Yellow dress and jacket trimmed with black; green hat; pale brown dog
Issued:	1981 - 1986
Varieties:	Also called Gilly
Series:	Vogue

Name	U.S. $	Can. $	U.K. £
Miss 1928	525.00	600.00	295.00

Miss 1929

Designer:	John Bromley
Height:	8", 20.3 cm
Colour:	Lavender dress and hat; white cat
Issued:	1982 - 1986
Varieties:	Also called Celia
Series:	Vogue

Name	U.S. $	Can. $	U.K. £
Miss 1929	525.00	600.00	295.00

Miss Charlotte

Designer: Jack Glynn
Height: 6", 15.0 cm
Colour: White and mauve dress with purple ribbon; white parasol with gold stem and bow
Issued: 1996 in a limited edition of 15,000
Series: Victorian Elegance

Name	U.S. $	Can. $	U.K. £
Miss Charlotte	140.00	160.00	80.00

Note: Commissioned by Compton and Woodhouse.

Miss Emily

Designer: Jack Glynn
Height: 6", 15.0 cm
Colour: Dark green jacket; light green and cream skirt; green bonnet with pink flowers; white parasol with gold stem
Issued: 1996 in a limited edition of 15,000
Series: Victorian Elegance

Name	U.S. $	Can. $	U.K. £
Miss Emily	140.00	160.00	80.00

Note: Commissioned by Compton and Woodhouse.

Miss Jane

Designer: Jack Glynn
Height: 6", 15.0 cm
Colour: Dark and light blue and white dress; white hat with blue ribbon; bouquet of flowers
Issued: 1996 in a limited edition of 15,000
Series: Victorian Elegance

Name	U.S. $	Can. $	U.K. £
Miss Jane	140.00	160.00	80.00

Note: Commissioned by Compton and Woodhouse.

Miss Laetita

Designer:	Jack Glynn
Height:	6", 15.0 cm
Colour:	Purple and lilac dress; purple hat with white feather; lilac parasol with gold stem
Issued:	1996 in a limited edition of 15,000
Series:	Victorian Elegance

Name	U.S. $	Can. $	U.K. £
Miss Laetita	140.00	160.00	80.00

Note: Commissioned by Compton and Woodhouse.

Miss Sarah

Designer:	Jack Glynn
Height:	6", 15.0 cm
Colour:	Deep red and rose overdress; white underskirt with rose bows; rose and white parasol with gold stem
Issued:	1996 in a limited edition of 15,000
Series:	Victorian Elegance

Name	U.S. $	Can. $	U.K. £
Miss Sarah	140.00	160.00	80.00

Note: Commissioned by Compton and Woodhouse.

Moira

Designer:	John Bromley
Modeller:	John Bromley
Height:	7 ½", 19.1 cm
Colour:	Blue and grey
Issued:	1987
Varieties:	Also called Davina; Janet
Series:	Ladies of Fashion

Name	U.S. $	Can. $	U.K. £
Moira	250.00	290.00	145.00

Note: Commissioned by Grattan Home Shopping.

Molly

Designer:	Unknown
Modeller:	Andy Moss
Height:	5 ¾", 14.6 cm
Colour:	Light peach and brown (porcelain)
Issued:	1997 to the present
Series:	Beau Monde

Name	U.S. $	Can. $	U.K. £
Molly	125.00	195.00	57.50

Monday's Child

Designer:	John Bromley
Height:	7 ¼", 18.4 cm
Colour:	Pink and white
Issued:	1989 - 1990
Series:	Children of the Week

Name	U.S. $	Can. $	U.K. £
Monday's Child	250.00	290.00	145.00

Monique

Designer:	Unknown
Modeller:	John Bromley
Height:	7 ¼", 18.5 cm
Colour:	Mottled blue
Issued:	1975 - 1977
Varieties:	Also called Christine (Style One); Petite
Series:	Ladies of Fashion

Name	U.S. $	Can. $	U.K. £
Monique	285.00	325.00	165.00

Montpellier Walk

Designer: Elizabeth Greenshields
Modeller: Martin Evans
Height: 8 ½", 21.6 cm
Colour: Yellow and peach (porcelain)
Issued: 1992 to the present
Series: Age of Elegance

Name	U.S. $	Can. $	U.K. £
Montpellier Walk	300.00	445.00	160.00

Moonlight

Designer: John Bromley
Modeller: John Bromley
Height: 8 ¼", 21.0 cm
Colour: Cream
Issued: 1995 in a limited edition of 1,000
Series: English Rose

Name	U.S. $	Can. $	U.K. £
Moonlight	650.00	995.00	395.00

Moonlight Serenade

Designer: John Bromley
Modeller: John Bromley
Height: 9 ½", 24.0 cm
Colour: Ivory
Issued: 1991 in a limited edition of 12,500
Series: Screen Goddesses

Name	U.S. $	Can. $	U.K. £
Moonlight Serenade	175.00	200.00	100.00

Note: Commissioned by Compton and Woodhouse.

Moonlit Rendezvous

Designer:	Elizabeth Greenshields
Modeller:	Jack Glynn
Height:	8 ¼", 21.0 cm
Colour:	Lavender (porcelain)
Issued:	1993 to the present
Varieties:	Also called Peaches and Cream
Series:	Age of Elegance

Name	U.S. $	Can. $	U.K. £
Moonlit Rendezvous	250.00	365.00	125.00

Mother's Day

Designer:	Timothy Potts
Modeller:	Timothy Potts
Height:	7 ¼", 18.4 cm
Colour:	Blue and pink
Issued:	1992 in a limited edition of 2,000
Series:	Togetherness

Name	U.S. $	Can. $	U.K. £
Mother's Day	350.00	650.00	245.00

Mountainman (The)

Designer:	John Bromley
Height:	13", 32.5 cm
Colour:	Yellow and brown
Issued:	1978 in a limited edition of 350

Name	U.S. $	Can. $	U.K. £
Mountainman (The)	2,100.00	2,500.00	1,250.00

Mrs. Fitzherbert

Designer:	Raymond Hughes
Modeller:	John Bromley
Height:	8 ¼", 21.0 cm
Colour:	Lilac overdress; cream underskirt with pink, yellow and blue flowers; cream bonnet with red bow, cream and gold feathers; gold highlights
Issued:	1993 in a limited edition of 12,500
Series:	Femmes Fatales

Name	U.S. $	Can. $	U.K. £
Mrs. Fitzherbert	280.00	325.00	160.00

Note: Commissioned by Compton and Woodhouse.

Mrs. Patrick Campbell as Juliet

Designer:	John Bromley
Height:	10 ½", 26.7 cm
Colour:	Rose-pink dress and cap
Issued:	1980 in a limited edition of 500
Series:	Famous Shakespeare Roles

Name	U.S. $	Can. $	U.K. £
Mrs. Patrick Campbell	550.00	650.00	325.00

Muffin Man

Designer:	Margaret Whittaker
Height:	8", 20.3 cm
Colour:	Black waistcoat, trousers, hat and shoes; light brown shirt; white apron; brown tray of muffins
Issued:	1977 - c.1980
Series:	Old London Streets

Name	U.S. $	Can. $	U.K. £
Muffin Man	340.00	400.00	195.00

Mummy's Little Helper

Designer: Timothy Potts
Modeller: Timothy Potts
Height: 8 ¼", 21.0 cm
Colour: Peach
Issued: 1993 in a limited edition of 2,000
Series: Togetherness

Name	U.S. $	Can. $	U.K. £
Mummy's Little Helper	325.00	575.00	195.00

Music Seller (The)

Designer: Robert Worthington
Height: 8", 20.3 cm
Colour: Blue jacket and cap; brown trousers
Issued: 1982 - 1985
Series: Character Collection

Name	U.S. $	Can. $	U.K. £
Music Seller (The)	340.00	400.00	195.00

My Dearest Emma

Designer: Basia Zarzycka
Modeller: Jack Glynn
Height: 9 ½", 24.0 cm
Colour: Cream skirt; gold lace corset bustier; bouquet of flowers
Issued: 1997 to the present
Series: Basia Zarzycka Collection

Name	U.S. $	Can. $	U.K. £
My Dearest Emma	400.00	595.00	200.00

My Love

Designer: John Bromley
Modeller: John Bromley
Height: 5 ¼", 13.3 cm
Colour: Red and purple
Issued: 1994 - 1994
Series: Valentine Debutante of the Year

Name	U.S. $	Can. $	U.K. £
My Love	165.00	175.00	95.00

My Pal

Designer: David Lyttleton
Height: 6", 15.0 cm
Colour: Blue and white sailor suit; white and brown dog
Issued: 1996 in a limited edition of 7,500
Series: Faye Whittaker's Childhood Memories Collection

Name	U.S. $	Can. $	U.K. £
My Pal	160.00	180.00	90.00

Note: Commissioned by Compton and Woodhouse.

My Pearl Wedding Day

Designer: John Bromley
Modeller: John Bromley
Height: 8", 20.3 cm
Colour: Pearl and pink
Issued: Unknown
Varieties: Also called Geraldine; My Ruby Wedding Day; My Silver Wedding Day
Series: Wedding Anniversary Collection

Name	U.S. $	Can. $	U.K. £
My Pearl Wedding Day	285.00	325.00	165.00

My Ruby Wedding Day

Designer: John Bromley
Modeller: John Bromley
Height: 8", 20.3 cm
Colour: Burgundy
Issued: Unknown
Varieties: Also called Geraldine; My Pearl Wedding Day; My Silver Wedding Day
Series: Wedding Anniversary Collection

Name	U.S. $	Can. $	U.K. £
My Ruby Wedding Day	285.00	325.00	165.00

My Silver Wedding Day

Designer: John Bromley
Modeller: John Bromley
Height: 8", 20.3 cm
Colour: Silver
Issued: Unknown
Varieties: Also called Geraldine; My Pearl Wedding Day; My Ruby Wedding Day
Series: Wedding Anniversary Collection

Name	U.S. $	Can. $	U.K. £
My Silver Wedding Day	285.00	325.00	165.00

My Teddy

Designer: Pauline Shone
Height: 7 ½", 19.1 cm
Colour: White and yellow
Issued: 1979 - unknown
Series: Children Studies

Name	U.S. $	Can. $	U.K. £
My Teddy	285.00	325.00	165.00

"Name Your Own"

Designer: Jack Glynn
Height: 8 ½", 21.6 cm
Colour: Red
Issued: 1996
Varieties: Also called Elaine (Style Two); Summer Breeze (Style Two)
Series: Ladies of Fashion

Name	U.S. $	Can. $	U.K. £
"Name Your Own"	215.00	250.00	125.00

Note: Commissioned by G.U.S. Home Shopping.

Nanette
Style One

Designer: Unknown
Height: Unknown
Colour: Unknown
Issued: 1982 - 1983
Series: Little Women

Name	U.S. $	Can. $	U.K. £
Nanette (Style One)	165.00	190.00	95.00

Photograph not available at press time

Nanette
Style Two

Designer: John Bromley
Modeller: John Bromley
Height: 5", 12.7 cm
Colour: White
Issued: 1982 - 1985
Varieties: Also called Estelle (Style Two); Jennifer (Style Two); Nicolette (Style Two); Paulette (Style Two)
Series: Debutante Collection

Name	U.S. $	Can. $	U.K. £
Nanette (Style Two)	150.00	170.00	85.00

Natalie
Style One

Designer:	John Bromley
Modeller:	John Bromley
Height:	5", 12.7 cm
Colour:	Peach
Issued:	1983 - 1989
Varieties:	Also called June; Justine; Samantha; Sophie (Style One); Tessa
Series:	Debutante Collection

Name	U.S. $	Can. $	U.K. £
Natalie (Style One)	130.00	150.00	75.00

Natalie
Style Two

Designer:	Martin Evans
Modeller:	Martin Evans
Height:	3 ¾", 9.5 cm
Colour:	Pale turquoise
Issued:	1995 to the present
Varieties:	Also called Kimberley (Style Two)
Series:	Minuettes

Name	U.S. $	Can. $	U.K. £
Natalie (Style Two)	50.00	69.50	30.00

Nefertiti

Designer:	John Bromley
Height:	Unknown
Colour:	Unknown
Issued:	1977 in a limited edition of 250
Series:	Egyptian Busts

Name	U.S. $	Can. $	U.K. £
Nefertiti	525.00	600.00	300.00

Photograph not available at press time

Nell Gwynn

Designer:	Raymond Hughes
Modeller:	John Bromley
Height:	8 ¼", 21.0 cm
Colour:	Yellow and cream dress with orange bows; basket of oranges
Issued:	1990 in a limited edition of 12,500
Series:	Femmes Fatales

Name	U.S. $	Can. $	U.K. £
Nell Gwynn	280.00	325.00	160.00

Note: Commissioned by Compton and Woodhouse

News Sheet Seller (The)

Designer:	Robert Worthington
Height:	7", 17.8 cm
Colour:	Jade jacket and cap; black trousers and shoes
Issued:	1982 - 1985
Series:	Character Collection

Name	U.S. $	Can. $	U.K. £
News Sheet Seller (The)	340.00	400.00	195.00

Nicola

Designer:	Graham Miller
Height:	10", 25.4 cm
Colour:	Pale blue
Issued:	1993 to the present
Varieties:	Also called Lydia (Style Two)
Series:	Silhouettes

Name	U.S. $	Can. $	U.K. £
Nicola	150.00	235.00	72.50

Nicole

Designer:	Helen Buckley
Modeller:	John Bromley
Height:	8 ¼", 21.0 cm
Colour:	White dress with pink flowers
Issued:	1988 - 1990
Series:	Ladies of Fashion

Name	U.S. $	Can. $	U.K. £
Nicole	280.00	325.00	160.00

Photograph not available at press time

Nicolette
Style One

Designer:	Unknown
Height:	Unknown
Colour:	Unknown
Issued:	1982 - 1983
Series:	Little Women

Name	U.S. $	Can. $	U.K. £
Nicolette (Style One)	165.00	190.00	95.00

Nicolette
Style Two

Designer:	John Bromley
Height:	5", 12.7 cm
Colour:	Brown
Issued:	1982 - 1985
Varieties:	Also called Estelle (Style Two); Jennifer (Style Two); Nanette (Style Two); Paulette (Style Two)
Series:	Debutante Collection

Name	U.S. $	Can. $	U.K. £
Nicolette (Style Two)	165.00	190.00	95.00

Night at the Opera

Designer: David Shilling
Modeller: John Bromley
Height: 8 ¾", 22.2 cm
Colour: Rose-pink and grey
Issued: 1987 in a limited edition of 1,000
Series: Designer Series

Name	U.S. $	Can. $	U.K. £
Night at the Opera	650.00	750.00	375.00

Nina

Designer: John Bromley
Modeller: John Bromley
Height: 5", 12.7 cm
Colour: Blue
Issued: 1993 to the present
Series: Debutante Collection

Name	U.S. $	Can. $	U.K. £
Nina	100.00	150.00	52.50

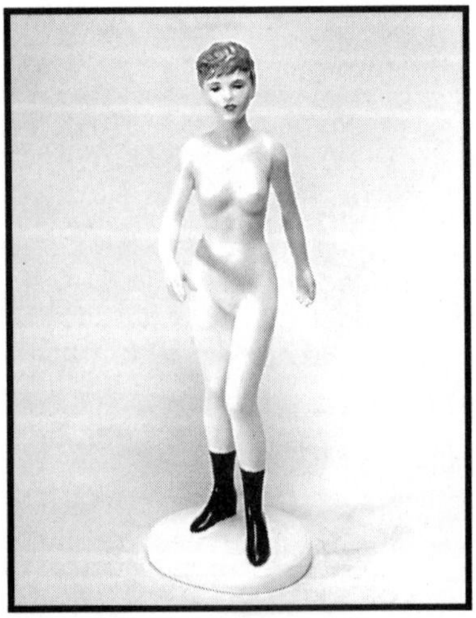

Nisbet Costumed Figure

Designer: John Bromley
Height: 8 ¾", 22.2 cm
Colour: Flesh tones
Issued: 1985 - 1988

Name	U.S. $	Can. $	U.K. £
Nisbet Costumed Figure	215.00	250.00	125.00

Note: Commissioned by the House of Nisbet Ltd.

Norma

Designer: Unknown
Height: Unknown
Colour: Unknown
Issued: 1986
Series: Ladies of Fashion

Name	U.S. $	Can. $	U.K. £
Norma	285.00	325.00	165.00

Note: Commissioned by Grattan Home Shopping.

Photograph not available at press time

Nude, Seated

Designer: John Bromley
Height: 6", 15.0 cm
Colour: Flesh tones
Issued: 1979 - 1982

Name	U.S. $	Can. $	U.K. £
Nude, Seated	340.00	400.00	195.00

Nude, Standing

Designer: John Bromley
Height: 8 ¾", 22.2 cm
Colour: Flesh tones; white cloth
Issued: 1979 - 1982

Name	U.S. $	Can. $	U.K. £
Nude, Standing	340.00	400.00	195.00

Nurse

Designer:	John Bromley
Height:	8 ½", 21.6 cm
Colour:	Pink
Issued:	1987 in a limited edition of 500
Series:	Nurses

Name	U.S. $	Can. $	U.K. £
Nurse	425.00	500.00	245.00

Note: Commissioned by the Hospital for Sick Children, London to commemorate the Golden Jubilee of the Nurses League.

Officer, 18th Hussars 1814

Designer:	Unknown
Height:	8 ½", 21.6 cm
Colour:	Dark blue and silver tunic; white trouser (porcelain)
Issued:	1990 in a limited edition of 1,000
Series:	Battle of Waterloo Collection

Name	U.S. $	Can. $	U.K. £
Officer, 18th Hussars 1814	525.00	600.00	295.00

Photograph not available at press time

Old Lady Feeding Pigeons

Designer:	Pamela Ware
Height:	Unknown
Colour:	Unknown
Issued:	1976 - unknown
Series:	Old London Streets

Name	U.S. $	Can. $	U.K. £
Old Lady Feeding Pigeons	395.00	450.00	225.00

Olivia
Style One

Designer: Elizabeth Greenshields
Modeller: Martin Evans
Height: 5 ¾", 14.6 cm
Colour: Peach and lavender (porcelain)
Issued: 1992 - 1993
Series: Beau Monde

Name	U.S. $	Can. $	U.K. £
Olivia (Style One)	165.00	190.00	95.00

Olivia
Style Two

Designer: Graham Miller
Modeller: Unknown
Height: 10", 25.4 cm
Colour: Pink
Issued: 1997 to the present
Varieties: Also called Philippa (Style Two)
Series: Silhouettes

Name	U.S. $	Can. $	U.K. £
Olivia (Style Two)	150.00	235.00	72.50

Olivia
Style Three

Designer: Maureen Halson
Height: 8 ¼", 21.0 cm
Colour: White and pink crinoline dress; gold jewellery and trim
Issued: 1997 - 1997
Series: Coalport Heirloom Figurine of the Year 1997

Name	U.S. $	Can. $	U.K. £
Olivia (Style Three)	280.00	325.00	160.00

Note: Commissioned by Compton and Woodhouse.

Olympic Runner

Designer: John Bromley
Height: 8 ½", 21.6 cm
Colour: White
Issued: 1983 in a limited edition of 250

Name	U.S. $	Can. $	U.K. £
Olympic Runner	300.00	350.00	175.00

Note: Commissioned by Wallcave.

On The Balcony

Designer: Elizabeth Greenshields
Modeller: Jack Glynn
Height: 7 ¼", 18.4 cm
Colour: Turquoise (porcelain)
Issued: 1994 to the present
Varieties: Also called Martha Rose
Series: Age of Elegance

Name	U.S. $	Can. $	U.K. £
On The Balcony	250.00	365.00	145.00

Opening Night

Designer: Elizabeth Greenshields
Modeller: Martin Evans
Height: 8", 20.3 cm
Colour: Lilac and blue (porcelain)
Issued: 1991 - 1995
Series: Age of Elegance

Name	U.S. $	Can. $	U.K. £
Opening Night	325.00	395.00	175.00

Opera at Glyndebourne

Designer:	Unknown
Height:	5 ½", 14.0 cm
Colour:	Pink, white and red (lustre)
Issued:	1994 - 1994
Series:	Debutante of the Year

Name	U.S. $	Can. $	U.K. £
Opera at Glyndebourne	200.00	175.00	110.00

Operetta

Designer:	Elizabeth Greenshields
Modeller:	Jack Glynn
Height:	8 ¼", 21.0 cm
Colour:	Lilac and white (porcelain)
Issued:	1991 - 1993
Series:	Age of Elegance

Name	U.S. $	Can. $	U.K. £
Operetta	375.00	445.00	175.00

Ophelia

Designer:	Elizabeth Greenshields
Modeller:	John Bromley
Height:	10", 25.4 cm
Colour:	White
Issued:	1980 - 1982
Series:	Characters from Shakespeare

Name	U.S. $	Can. $	U.K. £
Ophelia	475.00	550.00	275.00

Oranges and Lemons

Designer: John Bromley
Height: 8 ½", 21.6 cm
Colour: Green bodice with white neckline and sleeve cuffs, purple bows; lilac skirt
Issued: 1996 in a limited edition of 9,500
Series: The Cries of London

Name	U.S. $	Can. $	U.K. £
Oranges and Lemons	280.00	325.00	160.00

Note: Commissioned by Compton and Woodhouse.

Pageboy

Designer: Unknown
Height: 6", 15.0 cm
Colour: Dark blue jacket, pale blue trousers
Issued: 1992 in a limited edition of 1,500
Series: Wedding Collection

Name	U.S. $	Can. $	U.K. £
Pageboy	195.00	220.00	110.00

Pamela
Style One

Designer: John Bromley
Modeller: John Bromley
Height: 5", 12.7 cm
Colour: Pale green
Issued: 1983 - 1988
Varieties: Also called Andrea; Claire (Style One); Maxine; Susan (Style One)
Series: Debutante Collection

Name	U.S. $	Can. $	U.K. £
Pamela (Style One)	150.00	175.00	85.00

Pamela
Style Two

Designer: John Bromley
Modeller: John Bromley
Height: 8 ¼", 21.0 cm
Colour: Blue
Issued: 1996 - 1996
Series: Special Events

Name	U.S. $	Can. $	U.K. £
Pamela (Style Two)	250.00	295.00	170.00

Panache

Designer: Elizabeth Greenshields
Modeller: John Bromley
Height: 7 ¼", 18.4 cm
Colour: Pink and white
Issued: 1991 - 1993
Varieties: Also called Poise
Series: Chantilly Lace

Name	U.S. $	Can. $	U.K. £
Panache	300.00	350.00	175.00

Pansy

Designer: Jack Glynn
Height: 3 ½", 8.9 cm
Colour: Lilac overdress; cream underskirt with pink and purple pansies; gold trimming
Issued: 1993 in a limited edition of 15,000
Series: Fairest Flowers

Name	U.S. $	Can. $	U.K. £
Pansy	125.00	140.00	70.00

Note: Commissioned by Compton and Woodhouse.

Party Time

Designer: John Bromley
Modeller: John Bromley
Height: 4 ¾", 12.1 cm
Colour: Peach and white
Issued: 1990 - 1994
Varieties: Also called Rosie (Style One)
Series: Debutante Collection

Name	U.S. $	Can. $	U.K. £
Party Time	130.00	150.00	75.00

Patricia
Style One

Designer: John Bromley
Height: 8 ½", 21.6 cm
Colour: Yellow
Issued: 1976 - 1982
Varieties: Also called Charlotte (Style One); Michele
Series: Ladies of Fashion

Name	U.S. $	Can. $	U.K. £
Patricia (Style One)	300.00	350.00	175.00

Patricia
Style Two

Designer: Helen Buckley
Modeller: Martin Evans
Height: 6 ½", 16.5 cm
Colour: Purple
Issued: 1996 to the present
Series: Ladies of Fashion

Name	U.S. $	Can. $	U.K. £
Patricia (Style Two)	250.00	325.00	115.00

Paulette
Style One

Designer: Unknown
Height: Unknown
Colour: Unknown
Issued: 1982 - 1983
Series: Little Women

Name	U.S. $	Can. $	U.K. £
Paulette (Style One)	175.00	200.00	100.00

Photograph not available at press time

Paulette
Style Two

Designer: John Bromley
Modeller: John Bromley
Height: 5", 12.7 cm
Colour: Pale blue
Issued: 1982 - 1985
Varieties: Also called Estelle (Style Two); Jennifer (Style Two); Nanette (Style Two); Nicolette (Style Two)
Series: Debutante Collection

Name	U.S. $	Can. $	U.K. £
Paulette (Style Two)	165.00	190.00	95.00

Pauline

Designer: Shirley Curzon
Modeller: Martin Evans
Height: 8", 20.3 cm
Colour: Sea-green
Issued: 1997 to the present
Varieties: Also called Emma Jane
Series: Ladies of Fashion

Name	U.S. $	Can. $	U.K. £
Pauline	200.00	295.00	100.00

Pearl

Designer:	Elizabeth Greenshields
Modeller:	John Bromley
Height:	7 ¼", 18.4 cm
Colour:	White and pale blue with gold highlights
Issued:	1991 - 1993
Varieties:	Also called Velvet
Series:	Chantilly Lace

Name	U.S. $	Can. $	U.K. £
Pearl	250.00	290.00	145.00

Peep Bo

Designer:	Unknown
Height:	Unknown
Colour:	Unknown
Issued:	1979 - 1981
Series:	Gilbert and Sullivan

Name	U.S. $	Can. $	U.K. £
Peep Bo	500.00	600.00	295.00

Photograph not available at press time

Peaches and Cream

Designer:	Elizabeth Greenshields
Modeller:	Jack Glynn
Height:	8", 20.3 cm
Colour:	Peach and cream (porcelain)
Issued:	1995 - unknown
Varieties:	Also called Moonlit Rendezvous
Series:	Ladies of Fashion

Name	U.S. $	Can. $	U.K. £
Peaches and Cream	285.00	325.00	165.00

Note: Commissioned by Henderson's, Scotland; Peter Jones China Ltd., Wakefield; Collectables, Gateshead.

Peggy

Designer:	John Bromley
Modeller:	John Bromley
Height:	8", 20.3 cm
Colour:	Red dress with white collar
Issued:	1988 - 1990
Varieties:	Also called Julia (Style One); Sally Anne (Style Two)
Series:	Ladies of Fashion

Name	U.S. $	Can. $	U.K. £
Peggy	250.00	290.00	145.00

Penelope
Style Two

Designer:	John Bromley
Modeller:	John Bromley
Height:	5 ¼", 13.3 cm
Colour:	Dark green coat; cream underskirt
Issued:	1985 - 1988
Varieties:	Also called Eleanor (Style One); Grace (Style One)
Series:	Debutante Collection

Name	U.S. $	Can. $	U.K. £
Penelope (Style Two)	160.00	180.00	90.00

Penelope Ann

Designer:	Helen Buckley
Modeller:	John Bromley
Height:	8 ½", 21.6 cm
Colour:	Yellow and peach
Issued:	1991 to the present
Series:	Ladies of Fashion

Name	U.S. $	Can. $	U.K. £
Penelope Ann	275.00	425.00	135.00

Penny

Designer: John Bromley
Modeller: John Bromley
Height: 5 ¼", 13.3 cm
Colour: White with gold trim
Issued: 1987 - 1992
Varieties: Also called Carla; Catriona
Series: Debutante Collection

Name	U.S. $	Can. $	U.K. £
Penny	130.00	150.00	75.00

Petite

Designer: John Bromley
Modeller: John Bromley
Height: 7 ¼", 18.5 cm
Colour: Yellow dress with flowers
Issued: 1975 - 1977
Varieties: Also called Christine (Style One); Monique
Series: Ladies of Fashion

Name	U.S. $	Can. $	U.K. £
Petite	325.00	375.00	185.00

Petticoat Lane

Designer: Elizabeth Greenshields
Modeller: Brian Diment
Height: 8", 20.3 cm
Colour: Blue and yellow (porcelain)
Issued: 1992 - 1993
Series: Age of Elegance

Name	U.S. $	Can. $	U.K. £
Petticoat Lane	325.00	425.00	185.00

Petunia

Designer: Jack Glynn
Height: 3 ½", 8.9 cm
Colour: Deep pink dress with white underskirt; pink flowers on skirt; deep pink hat; gold trim
Issued: 1993 in a limited edition of 15,000
Series: Fairest Flowers

Name	U.S. $	Can. $	U.K. £
Petunia	125.00	140.00	70.00

Note: Commissioned by Compton and Woodhouse.

Philippa
Style One

Designer: John Bromley
Modeller: John Bromley
Height: 8", 20.3 cm
Colour: White dress with yellow and red roses
Issued: 1988 - 1989
Varieties: Also called Debbie; Gillian (Style One); Linda (Style One); Melody
Series: Ladies of Fashion

Name	U.S. $	Can. $	U.K. £
Philippa (Style One)	385.00	440.00	220.00

Philippa
Style Two

Designer: Graham Miller
Modeller: Unknown
Height: 10", 25.4 cm
Colour: Pale blue
Issued: 1993 to the present
Varieties: Also called Olivia (Style Two)
Series: Silhouettes

Name	U.S. $	Can. $	U.K. £
Philippa (Style Two)	125.00	235.00	72.50

Photograph not available at press time

Philomena

Designer: John Bromley
Height: Unknown
Colour: Unknown
Issued: 1987 in a limited edition of 250
Series: Edwardian Beauties

Name	U.S. $	Can. $	U.K. £
Philomena	300.00	350.00	175.00

Phoebe

Designer: Andrea Cox
Modeller: Jack Glynn
Height: 12", 30.5 cm
Colour: Light brown dress; orange shawl; buff dog
Issued: 1997 to the present
Series: The Roaring Twenties (Style Two)

Name	U.S. $	Can. $	U.K. £
Pheobe	300.00	550.00	140.00

Pie Maker (The)

Designer: Robert Worthington
Height: 8", 20.3 cm
Colour: Green jacket and cap; brown waistcoat and trousers
Issued: 1982 - 1985
Series: Character Collection

Name	U.S. $	Can. $	U.K. £
Pie Maker (The)	340.00	400.00	195.00

Pirate Captain

Designer: Margaret Whittaker
Height: 8 ½", 21.6 cm
Colour: Blue and cream
Issued: 1977 - 1981
Series: Gilbert and Sullivan

Name	U.S. $	Can. $	U.K. £
Pirate Captain	550.00	650.00	325.00

Pitti Sing

Designer: Unknown
Height: 8", 20.3 cm
Colour: Turquoise and sea-green
Issued: 1979 - 1981
Series: Gilbert and Sullivan

Name	U.S. $	Can. $	U.K. £
Pitti Sing	550.00	650.00	325.00

Poacher (The)

Designer: Robert Worthington
Height: 8", 20.3 cm
Colour: Green trousers; brown vest and cap
Issued: 1982 - 1985
Series: Character Collection

Name	U.S. $	Can. $	U.K. £
Poacher (The)	325.00	375.00	185.00

Pochahontas

Designer: John Bromley
Height: 7 ¼", 18.4 cm
Colour: Tan buckskins
Issued: 1982 - unknown

Name	U.S. $	Can. $	U.K. £
Pochahontas	395.00	450.00	225.00

Poise

Designer: Elizabeth Greenshields
Modeller: John Bromley
Height: 7 ¼", 18.4 cm
Colour: White and yellow
Issued: 1991 - 1993
Varieties: Also called Panache
Series: Chantilly Lace

Name	U.S. $	Can. $	U.K. £
Poise	300.00	350.00	175.00

Policeman (The)

Designer: Margaret Whittaker
Height: 8 ¼", 21 cm
Colour: Blue
Issued: 1979 - 1981
Series: Gilbert and Sullivan

Name	U.S. $	Can. $	U.K. £
Policeman (The)	525.00	600.00	295.00

Polly

Designer:	John Bromley
Modeller:	John Bromley
Height:	6 ½", 16.5 cm
Colour:	Pink
Issued:	1977 - 1988
Varieties:	Also called Elizabeth (Style One); Lisa (Style One)
Series:	Ladies of Fashion

Name	U.S. $	Can. $	U.K. £
Polly	300.00	350.00	175.00

Polonaise Walk

Designer:	Helen Buckley
Modeller:	Jack Glynn
Height:	9", 22.9 cm
Colour:	Pale yellow and pale green (porcelain)
Issued:	1997 to the present
Series:	Age of Elegance

Name	U.S. $	Can. $	U.K. £
Polonaise Walk	225.00	395.00	140.00

Pontefract Princess

Designer:	Helen Buckley
Modeller:	David Lyttleton
Height:	6 ¼", 15.9 cm
Colour:	Rose-pink and white
Issued:	1996 in a limited edition of 200
Varieties:	Also called Chelsea Reception
Series:	Ladies of Fashion

Name	U.S. $	Can. $	U.K. £
Pontefract Princess	175.00	200.00	99.95

Note: Commissioned by Peter Jones China Ltd., Wakefield.

Poppy
Style One

Designer:	Helen Buckley
Modeller:	John Bromley
Height:	4 ¾", 12.1 cm
Colour:	Red dress; white scarf
Issued:	1990 to the present
Varieties:	Also called April
Series:	Debutante Collection

Name	U.S. $	Can. $	U.K. £
Poppy (Style One)	100.00	160.00	52.50

Poppy
Style Two

Designer:	Jack Glynn
Height:	3 ½", 8.9 cm
Colour:	Grey overdress; white skirt with pink flowers; gold trimming
Issued:	1993 in a limited edition of 15,000
Series:	Fairest Flowers

Name	U.S. $	Can. $	U.K. £
Poppy (Style Two)	125.00	140.00	70.00

Note: Commissioned by Compton and Woodhouse.

Poppy Ball

Designer:	John Bromley
Modeller:	John Bromley
Height:	5", 12.7 cm
Colour:	Red
Issued:	1997 - 1997
Series:	Debutante of the Year

Name	U.S. $	Can. $	U.K. £
Poppy Ball	100.00	150.00	50.00

Precious Moments

Designer:	Val Littlewood
Modeller:	John Bromley
Height:	8 ½", 21.6 cm
Colour:	Yellow, pink and white
Issued:	1989 - 1991
Series:	Ladies of Leisure

Name	U.S. $	Can. $	U.K. £
Precious Moments	300.00	350.00	175.00

Present For Grandma (A)

Designer:	David Lyttleton
Height:	7 ¼", 18.4 cm
Colour:	Pale blue dress and cape; white overdress; tan and white dog
Issued:	1994 in a limited edition of 5,000
Series:	Barnardo's

Name	U.S. $	Can. $	U.K. £
Present For Grandma	160.00	180.00	90.00

Note: Commissioned by Compton and Woodhouse.

Pretty Jessica

Designer:	Helen Buckley
Modeller:	Jack Glynn
Height:	8 ¾", 22.2 cm
Colour:	Pink
Issued:	1998 in a limited edition of 1,000
Series:	English Rose

Name	U.S. $	Can. $	U.K. £
Pretty Jessica	375.00	495.00	200.00

Primrose

Designer: Jack Glynn
Height: 3 ½", 8.9 cm
Colour: Yellow overdress; white skirt with yellow flowers; yellow hat; gold trimming
Issued: 1993 in a limited edition of 15,000
Series: Fairest Flowers

Name	U.S. $	Can. $	U.K. £
Primrose	125.00	140.00	70.00

Note: Commissioned by Compton and Woodhouse.

Princess Alexandra

Designer: John Bromley
Height: 8 ½", 21.5 cm
Colour: White gown; pink roses; gold necklace and brooch
Issued: 1992 in a limited edition of 7,500
Series: Royal Brides

Name	U.S. $	Can. $	U.K. £
Princess Alexandra	265.00	300.00	150.00

Note: Commissioned by Compton and Woodhouse.

Prize Winner

Designer: Unknown
Height: Unknown
Colour: Brown trousers, waistcoat and hat; white shirt; green marrow
Issued: c.1979 - unknown

Name	U.S. $	Can. $	U.K. £
Prize Winner	425.00	500.00	250.00

Promenade (The)
Style One

Designer: Unknown
Height: Unknown
Colour: 1. Pale pink and white (porcelain)
2. Lilac
Issued: c.1976 - unknown

Colourways	U.S. $	Can. $	U.K. £
1. Pale pink	475.00	550.00	275.00
2. Lilac	475.00	550.00	275.00

Promenade
Style Two

Designer: Elizabeth Greenshields
Modeller: Brian Diment
Height: 8 ¼", 21.0 cm
Colour: Lavender
Issued: 1991 - 1994
Series: Age of Elegance

Name	U.S. $	Can. $	U.K. £
Promenade (Style Two)	300.00	350.00	175.00

Promenade à Cheval (La)

Designer: Margaret Whittaker
Modleler: John Bromley
Height: Unknown
Colour: Dark green habit; black hat; palomino horse
Issued: 1976 in a limited edition of 1,000

Name	U.S. $	Can. $	U.K. £
Promenade à Cheval (La)	700.00	800.00	400.00

Proposal (The)

Designer:	John Bromley
Height:	6 ½", 16.5 cm
Colour:	Lady - Pale lemon dress; Gentleman - Brown jacket; pink waistcoat; beige pantaloons
Issued:	1980 - 1983
Series:	Ladies of Fashion

Name	U.S. $	Can. $	U.K. £
Proposal (The)	425.00	500.00	245.00

Prudence

Designer:	John Bromley
Modeller:	John Bromley
Height:	5 ¼", 13.3 cm
Colour:	Pink
Issued:	1985 - 1988
Varieties:	Also called Beatrice (Style One); Hannah (Style One)
Series:	Debutante Collection

Name	U.S. $	Can. $	U.K. £
Prudence	150.00	170.00	85.00

Queen (The)
Style One
(on wooden plinth)

Designer:	John Bromley
Modeller:	John Bromley
Height:	8 ½", 21.6 cm
Colour:	White gown; bouquet of white orchids
Issued:	1994 in a limited edition of 7,500
Series:	Royal Brides

Name	U.S. $	Can. $	U.K. £
Queen (Style One)	280.00	325.00	160.00

Note: Commissioned by Compton and Woodhouse.

Queen Anne

Designer: Michael Abberley
Height: 8 ¼", 21 cm
Colour: Purple cloak; lilac dress
Issued: 1990 in a limited edition of 1,000
Series: Queens of England

Name	U.S. $	Can. $	U.K. £
Queen Anne	700.00	800.00	395.00

Queen Charlotte's Ball

Designer: Elizabeth Greenshields
Modeller: John Bromley
Height: 5", 12.7 cm
Colour: Pink
Issued: 1992 - 1992
Series: Debutante of the Year

Name	U.S. $	Can. $	U.K. £
Queen Charlotte's Ball	165.00	190.00	95.00

Queen Elizabeth I (1533-1603)

Designer: Michael Abberley
Height: 8 ¼", 21.0 cm
Colour: Green, white and pink
Issued: 1989 in a limited edition of 1,000
Series: Queens of England

Name	U.S. $	Can. $	U.K. £
Queen Elizabeth I (1533-1603)	700.00	800.00	395.00

Queen Mary
(on wooden plinth)

Designer: John Bromley
Height: 8 ½", 21.6 cm
Colour: White gown decorated with orange blossom; platinum jewellery
Issued: 1992 in a limited edition of 7,500
Serries: Royal Brides

Name	U.S. $	Can. $	U.K. £
Queen Mary	280.00	325.00	160.00

Note: Commissioned by Compton and Woodhouse.

Queen Mother (The)
Style One
(on wooden plinth)

Designer: John Bromley
Height: 8 ½", 21.6 cm
Colour: Ivory dress; yellow rose bouquet
Issued: 1993 in a limited edition of 7,500
Series: Royal Brides

Name	U.S. $	Can. $	U.K. £
Queen Mother (Style One)	280.00	325.00	160.00

Note: Commissioned by Compton and Woodhouse.

Queen of Sheba
(on wooden plinth)

Designer: David Cornell
Height: 9 ¼", 23.5 cm
Colour: Pale and dark blue dress with gold trimmings; white headdress
Issued: 1994 in a limited edition of 9,500
Series: Fabled Beauties

Name	U.S. $	Can. $	U.K. £
Queen of Sheba	300.00	350.00	175.00

Note: Commissioned by Compton and Woodhouse.

Queen Victoria
Style One

Designer: Michael Abberley
Height: 8 ¼", 21.0 cm
Colour: Blue and white
Issued: 1989 in a limited edition of 1,000
Series: Queens of England

Name	U.S. $	Can. $	U.K. £
Queen Victoria (Style One)	700.00	800.00	395.00

Queen Victoria
Style Two
(on wooden plinth)

Designer: John Bromley
Height: 8 ½", 21.6 cm
Colour: White gown; gold necklace and Royal Garter
Issued: 1991 in a limited edition of 7,500
Series: Royal Brides

Name	U.S. $	Can. $	U.K. £
Queen Victoria (Style Two)	280.00	325.00	160.00

Note: Commissioned by Compton and Woodhouse.

Rachel
Style One

Designer: John Bromley
Height: 8 ½", 21.6 cm
Colour: Dark blue and pale blue
Issued: 1976 - 1982
Varieties: Also called Christabel (Style One); Kate (Style One)
Series: Ladies of Fashion

Name	U.S. $	Can. $	U.K. £
Rachel (Style One)	325.00	375.00	185.00

Rachel
Style Two

Designer: Elizabeth Greenshields
Modeller: Martin Evans
Height: 5 ¾", 14.6 cm
Colour: Pink (porcelain)
Issued: 1993 to the present
Series: Beau Monde

Name	U.S. $	Can. $	U.K. £
Rachel (Style Two)	100.00	175.00	57.50

Radiance (Bride)

Designer: John Bromley
Height: 5", 12.7 cm
Colour: White with gold trim
Issued: 1984 - 1989
Series: Brides

Name	U.S. $	Can. $	U.K. £
Radiance	130.00	150.00	75.00

Raggetty Anne

Designer: David Lyttleton
Height: 6", 15.0 cm
Colour: Blue bodice; blue and white striped skirt
with pink flowers; straw hat
Issued: 1995 in a limited edition of 7,500
Series: Faye Whittaker's Childhood Memories Collection

Name	U.S. $	Can. $	U.K. £
Raggetty Anne	160.00	180.00	90.00

Note: Commissioned by Compton and Woodhouse.

Rake

Designer: Unknown
Height: 10", 25.4 cm
Colour: Blue coat and hat
Issued: c.1976 - unknown

Name	U.S. $	Can. $	U.K. £
Rake	300.00	350.00	175.00

Rapture

Designer: John Bromley
Modeller: John Bromley
Height: 8", 20.3 cm
Colour: Pale blue and green
Issued: 1984 - 1990
Varieties: Also called Katherine (Style One); Maureen; Rosalee; Spring Song
Series: Ladies of Fashion

Name	U.S. $	Can. $	U.K. £
Rapture	250.00	290.00	145.00

R.C.M.P.

Designer: Robert Worthington
Height: 9 ½", 24.0 cm
Colour: Red tunic; black trousers
Issued: 1982 in a limited edition of 950

Name	U.S. $	Can. $	U.K. £
R.C.M.P.	395.00	450.00	225.00

Note: Commissioned by Canadian Collector Plates, Milliken, Ontario. Original issue price $225.00.

Reaper (The)

Designer: John Bromley
Height: 8", 20.3 cm
Colour: Green, yellow and brown
Issued: 1984 in a limited edition of 1,000
Series: Arcadian Collection

Name	U.S. $	Can. $	U.K. £
Reaper (The)	340.00	400.00	195.00

Rebecca
Style One

Designer: John Bromley
Modeller: John Bromley
Height: 8 ½", 21.6 cm
Colour: Dark blue
Issued: 1976 - 1980
Varieties: Also called Candida; Roberta
Series: Ladies of Fashion

Name	U.S. $	Can. $	U.K. £
Rebecca (Style One)	300.00	350.00	175.00

Photograph not available at press time

Rebecca
Style Two

Designer: John Bromley
Height: Unknown
Colour: Unknown
Issued: 1987 in a limited edition of 250
Series: Edwardian Beauties

Name	U.S. $	Can. $	U.K. £
Rebecca (Style Two)	385.00	440.00	220.00

Rebecca
Style Three

Designer: Elizabeth Greenshields
Modeller: Martin Evans
Height: 5 ¼", 13.3 cm
Colour: Green and blue (porcelain)
Issued: 1992 - 1993
Series: Beau Monde

Name	U.S. $	Can. $	U.K. £
Rebecca (Style Three)	165.00	190.00	95.00

Rebecca
Style Four

Designer: Unknown
Height: Unknown
Colour: Pink gown; white hat with pink frill; gold trim
Issued: 1997 in a limited edition of 2,500
Series: Literary Heroines

Name	U.S. $	Can. $	U.K. £
Rebecca (Style Four)	275.00	425.00	160.00

Red Rose of Lancashire

Designer: Helen Buckley
Modeller: John Bromley
Height: 8 ½", 21.6 cm
Colour: Peach dress with red sash and rose; red rose headdress
Issued: 1997 in a limited edition of 500
Varieties: Also called Society Reception
Series: Ladies of Fashion

Name	U.S. $	Can. $	U.K. £
Red Rose of Lancashire	175.00	200.00	99.95

Note: Commissioned by Compton and Woodhouse.

Regents Park

Designer: Elizabeth Greenshields
Modeller: Martin Evans
Height: 8", 20.3 cm
Colour: Pale lavender and pale blue (porcelain)
Issued: 1992 to the present
Series: The Age of Elegance

Name	U.S. $	Can. $	U.K. £
Regents Park	275.00	425.00	160.00

Regina

Designer: John Bromley
Modeller: John Bromley
Height: 7", 17.8 cm
Colour: Blue dress with pink highlights
Issued: 1977 - 1991
Varieties: Also called Jean (Style One); Josephine; Serenade (Style One); Winsome
Series: Ladies of Fashion

Name	U.S. $	Can. $	U.K. £
Regina	265.00	300.00	150.00

Rendezvous in Rio

Modeller: John Bromley
Designer: David Shilling
Height: 9", 22.9 cm
Colour: Pink and peach
Issued: 1987 in a limited edition of 1,000
Series: Designer Series

Name	U.S. $	Can. $	U.K. £
Rendezvous in Rio	650.00	750.00	375.00

Repose

Designer: Pauline Shone
Height: Unknown
Colour: White
Issued: 1979 - unknown
Series: Children Studies

Name	U.S. $	Can. $	U.K. £
Repose	250.00	290.00	145.00

Restoration Stuart (1660 - 1689)

Designer: John Bromley
Height: 10", 25.5 cm
Colour: Burgundy, white and black
Issued: 1981 in a limited edition of 500
Series: History of Costume

Name	U.S. $	Can. $	U.K. £
Restoration Stuart (1660 - 1689)	875.00	1,000.00	500.00

Restoration Stuart (1685 - 1689)

Designer: Unknown
Height: Unknown
Colour: Unknown
Issued: 1979 in a limited edition of 500
Series: History of Costume

Name	U.S. $	Can. $	U.K. £
Restoration Stuart (1685-1689)	875.00	1,000.00	500.00

Photograph not available at press time

Rhian

Designer:	John Bromley
Modeller:	John Bromley
Height:	8", 20.3 cm
Colour:	Green and white
Issued:	1997 in a limited edition of 250
Series:	Welsh Ladies of Fashion

Name	U.S. $	Can. $	U.K. £
Rhian	175.00	200.00	99.95

Note: Commissioned by J. T. Morgan & Co. Ltd., Wales.

Richard II

Designer:	Robert Worthington
Height:	9 ¼", 23.5 cm
Colour:	Red and gold tunic; blue leotards
Issued:	1979 in a limited edition of 2,000
Series:	Characters from Shakespeare

Name	U.S. $	Can. $	U.K. £
Richard II	475.00	550.00	275.00

Riding Lesson (The)

Designer:	Pauline Shone
Height:	8 ½", 21.6 cm
Colour:	Cream, white, black and brown
Issued:	1979 - unknown
Series:	Children Studies

Name	U.S. $	Can. $	U.K. £
Riding Lesson (The)	280.00	325.00	160.00

Roberta

Designer: John Bromley
Modeller: John Bromley
Height: 8 ½", 21.6 cm
Colour: Yellow
Issued: 1976 - 1981
Varieties: Also called Candida; Rebecca (Style One)
Series: Ladies of Fashion

Name	U.S. $	Can. $	U.K. £
Roberta	300.00	350.00	175.00

Romance
Style One

Designer: John Bromley
Height: 8", 20.3 cm
Colour: Gentleman - Green jacket and breeches; rose-pink waistcoat
Woman - Cream dress with red roses; red and cream bodice
Issued: 1978 - 1982
Series: Ladies of Fashion

Name	U.S. $	Can. $	U.K. £
Romance (Style One)	475.00	550.00	275.00

Romance
Style Two

Designer: Elizabeth Greenshields
Modeller: John Bromley
Height: 7 ¼", 18.4 cm
Colour: Peach
Issued: 1992 - 1993
Varieties: Also called Chic; Silk
Series: Chantilly Lace

Name	U.S. $	Can. $	U.K. £
Romance (Style Two)	280.00	325.00	160.00

Romantic Bride

Designer: John Bromley and Douglas Tootle
Height: 8 ¼", 21.0 cm
Colour: White and yellow
Issued: 1989 - 1991
Varieties: Also called Wedding Day
Series: Brides

Name	U.S. $	Can. $	U.K. £
Romantic Bride	300.00	350.00	175.00

Romantic Seventies (The)

Designer: John Bromley
Modeller: John Bromley
Height: 9", 22.9 cm
Colour: Lady - pink dress with white frills and rose-pink flowers
Gentleman - white jacket with blue collar, cuffs, belt and sash; black trousers with red stripe
Issued: 1982 - 1984
Series: Dancing Years

Name	U.S. $	Can. $	U.K. £
Romantic Seventies (The)	500.00	600.00	295.00

Romany Dance

Designer: John Bromley
Modeller: John Bromley
Height: 8", 20.3 cm
Colour: Red
Issued: 1988 - 1993
Series: Ladies of Fashion

Name	U.S. $	Can. $	U.K. £
Romany Dance	280.00	325.00	160.00

Romeo and Juliet

Designer:	Robert Worthington
Height:	10", 25.4 cm
Colour:	Juliet - Pink gown Romeo - Green shirt, tabard and cap; turquoise leotards
Issued:	1981 - 1982
Series:	Characters from Shakespeare

Name	U.S. $	Can. $	U.K. £
Romeo and Juliet	700.00	800.00	395.00

Rosalee

Designer:	John Bromley
Height:	8", 20.3 cm
Colour:	Red dress with black markings
Issued:	1986
Varieties:	Also called Katherine (Style One); Maureen; Rapture; Spring Song
Series:	Ladies of Fashion

Name	U.S. $	Can. $	U.K. £
Rosalee	250.00	290.00	145.00

Note: Commissioned by Grattan Home Shopping.

Rosamund

Designer:	John Bromley
Modeller:	John Bromley
Height:	5", 12.7 cm
Colour:	Pale green and yellow
Issued:	1989 - 1991
Series:	Debutante Collection

Name	U.S. $	Can. $	U.K. £
Rosamund	130.00	150.00	75.00

Rose
Style One

Designer: Jack Glynn
Height: 3 ½", 8.9 cm
Colour: Red overdress; white underskirt with yellow and pink roses; beige hat with red ribbon; gold trim
Issued: 1993 in a limited edition of 15,000
Series: Fairest Flowers

Name	U.S. $	Can. $	U.K. £
Rose (Style One)	130.00	150.00	70.00

Note: Commissioned by Compton and Woodhouse.

Rose
Style Two

Designer: Jack Glynn
Height: 9", 22.9 cm
Colour: Pink crinoline gown and bonnet; bouquet of roses
Issued: 1994 in a limited edition of 12,500
Series: The Four Flowers Collection

Name	U.S. $	Can. $	U.K. £
Rose (Style Two)	280.00	325.00	160.00

Note: Commissioned by Compton and Woodhouse.

Rose
Style Three

Designer: Unknown
Modeller: Martin Evans
Height: 5 ½", 14.0 cm
Colour: Pale green and pink (porcelain)
Issued: 1995 to the present
Varieties: Also called Marie (Style Two)
Series: Beau Monde

Name	U.S. $	Can. $	U.K. £
Rose (Style Three)	100.00	150.00	57.50

Rose Ball

Designer:	John Bromley
Modeller:	John Bromley
Height:	4 ¾", 12.1 cm
Colour:	Orange lustre
Issued:	1995 - 1995
Series:	Debutante of the Year

Name	U.S. $	Can. $	U.K. £
Rose Ball	125.00	175.00	95.00

Rose Crescent

Designer:	Elizabeth Greenshields
Modeller:	Brian Diment
Height:	8", 20.3 cm
Colour:	Peach and lavender (porcelain)
Issued:	1992 - 1994
Series:	Age of Elegance

Name	U.S. $	Can. $	U.K. £
Rose Crescent	325.00	445.00	185.00

Rose Marie

Designer:	John Bromley
Modeller:	John Bromley
Height:	4 ½", 11.9 cm
Colour:	Peach
Issued:	1992 - 1994
Series:	Debutante Collection

Name	U.S. $	Can. $	U.K. £
Rose Marie	130.00	150.00	75.00

Rosemary
Style One

Designer: John Bromley
Modeller: John Bromley
Height: 7 ½", 19.1 cm
Colour: Red flowered dress
Issued: 1975 - 1989
Varieties: Also called Blanche (Style One); Collette
Series: Ladies of Fashion

Name	U.S. $	Can. $	U.K. £
Rosemary (Style One)	280.00	325.00	160.00

Rosemary
Style Two

Designer: Helen Buckley
Modeller: John Bromley
Height: 6 ¾", 17.2 cm
Colour: Blue
Issued: 1997 to the present
Varieties: Also called Lady in Lace
Series: Ladies of Fashion

Name	U.S. $	Can. $	U.K. £
Rosemary (Style Two)	195.00	220.00	110.00

Note: Commissioned by Home Farm Hampers.

Rosie
Style One

Designer: John Bromley
Modeller: John Bromley
Height: 4 ¾", 12.1 cm
Colour: White with gold highlights
Issued: 1991 - 1992
Varieties: Also called Party Time
Series: Debutante Collection

Name	U.S. $	Can. $	U.K. £
Rosie (Style One)	130.00	150.00	75.00

Rosie
Style Two

Designer: Unknown
Modeller: Martin Evans
Height: 3 ½", 8.9 cm
Colour: Pink
Issued: 1996 to the present
Varieties: Also called Jade
Series: Minuettes

Name	U.S. $	Can. $	U.K. £
Rosie (Style Two)	60.00	105.00	30.00

Royal Caledonian Ball

Designer: John Bromley
Modeller: John Bromley
Height: 5", 12.7 cm
Colour: Pale blue dress; dark blue tartan sash
Issued: 1993 - 1993
Series: Debutante of the Year

Name	U.S. $	Can. $	U.K. £
Royal Caledonian Ball	115.00	130.00	65.00

Royal Enclosure at Ascot

Designer: Elizabeth Greenshields
Modeller: Brian Diment
Height: 10", 25.4 cm
Colour: Lavender and pink (porcelain)
Issued: 1992 in a limited edition of 2,000
Series: Turn of the Century

Name	U.S. $	Can. $	U.K. £
Royal Enclosure at Ascot	600.00	700.00	350.00

Royal Gala

Designer:	Elizabeth Greenshields
Modeller:	Brian Diment
Height:	8", 20.3 cm
Colour:	Pink and blue (porcelain)
Issued:	1992 - 1996
Series:	Age of Elegance

Name	U.S. $	Can. $	U.K. £
Royal Gala	325.00	425.00	160.00

Ruby

Designer:	Maureen Halson
Height:	9 ¼", 23.5 cm
Colour:	Light to a deep rose dress; white flowers with gold leaves; gold necklace with ruby centre
Issued:	1992 in a limited edition of 9,500
Series:	Spirits of the Jewels

Name	U.S. $	Can. $	U.K. £
Ruby	325.00	425.00	160.00

Note: Commissioned by Compton and Woodhouse.

Ruth

Designer:	Elizabeth Greenshields
Modeller:	Brian Diment
Height:	5 ¼", 13.3 cm
Colour:	Yellow and orange (porcelain)
Issued:	1993 - 1994
Series:	Beau Monde

Name	U.S. $	Can. $	U.K. £
Ruth	150.00	170.00	85.00

Saddler (The)

Designer: Margaret Whittaker
Height: 7", 17.8 cm
Colour: Grey and black
Issued: 1974 - c.1980
Series: Craft Figures

Name	U.S. $	Can. $	U.K. £
Saddler (The)	300.00	350.00	175.00

Sadie

Designer: Andrea Cox
Modeller: Jack Glynn
Height: 12", 30.5 cm
Colour: Blue dress and pink fan
Issued: 1997 to the present
Series: The Roaring Twenties (Style Two)

Name	U.S. $	Can. $	U.K. £
Sadie	300.00	485.00	125.00

Sailor (The)

Designer: John Bromley
Height: 8 ½", 21.6 cm
Colour: Royal blue
Issued: 1984 in a limited edition of 1.500
Series: King and Country (1940 Period)

Name	U.S. $	Can. $	U.K. £
Sailor (The)	340.00	400.00	195.00

Sally

Designer:	Graham Miller
Modeller:	Unknown
Height:	10", 25.4 cm
Colour:	Pink
Issued:	1997 to the present
Varieties:	Also called Carole
Series:	Silhouettes

Name	U.S. $	Can. $	U.K. £
Sally	175.00	235.00	72.50

Sally Anne
Style One

Designer:	John Bromley
Modeller:	John Bromley
Height:	5", 12.7 cm
Colour:	Dark blue dress with white frill
Issued:	1988 - 1989
Varieties:	Also called Annette (Style Four); Claudette (Style Two); Jeanette (Style Two); Joanne (Style Two); Juliette (Style Two)
Series:	Ladies of Fashion

Name	U.S. $	Can. $	U.K. £
Sally Anne (Style One)	150.00	170.00	85.00

Note: Commissioned by Kays.

Sally Anne
Style Two

Designer:	John Bromley
Modeller:	John Bromley
Height:	8", 20.3 cm
Colour:	Green and white
Issued:	1988 - 1989
Varieties:	Also called Julia (Style One); Peggy
Series:	Ladies of Fashion

Name	U.S. $	Can. $	U.K. £
Sally Anne (Style Two)	250.00	290.00	145.00

Salome
(on wooden plinth)

Designer: David Cornell
Height: 9 ¾", 24.7 cm
Colour: Pink, blue and lilac; gold accessories
Issued: 1995 in a limited edition of 9,500
Series: Fabled Beauties

Name	U.S. $	Can. $	U.K. £
Salome	300.00	350.00	175.00

Note: Commissioned by Compton and Woodhouse.

Samantha

Designer: John Bromley
Modeller: John Bromley
Height: 5", 12.7 cm
Colour: White with gold trim
Issued: 1985 - 1991
Varieties: Also called June; Justine; Natalie (Style One); Sophie (Style One); Tessa
Series: Debutante Collection

Name	U.S. $	Can. $	U.K. £
Samantha	130.00	150.00	75.00

Sandra

Designer: John Bromley
Modeller: Andy Moss
Height: 4 ½", 11.9 cm
Colour: Blue
Issued: 1996 to the present
Series: Debutante Collection

Name	U.S. $	Can. $	U.K. £
Sandra	100.00	150.00	52.50

Sapphire

Designer:	Maureen Halson
Height:	9 ¼", 23.5 cm
Colour:	Lilac and mauve dress trimmed with gold; pink rose
Issued:	1991 in a limited edition of 9,500
Series:	Spirits of the Jewels

Name	U.S. $	Can. $	U.K. £
Sapphire	280.00	325.00	160.00

Note: Commissioned by Compton and Woodhouse.

Sarah
Style One

Designer:	John Bromley
Modeller:	John Bromley
Height:	8 ½", 21.6 cm
Colour:	Lavender
Issued:	1975 - 1987
Varieties:	Also called Annabelle (Style One); Lucy (Style One)
Series:	Ladies of Fashion

Name	U.S. $	Can. $	U.K. £
Sarah (Style One)	285.00	325.00	165.00

Sarah
Style Two

Designer:	Elizabeth Greenshields
Modeller:	Jack Glynn
Height:	8 ¼", 21.0 cm
Colour:	Pink
Issued:	1994 - 1994
Series:	Figurine of the Year

Name	U.S. $	Can. $	U.K. £
Sarah (Style Two)	425.00	500.00	250.00

Sarah Jane

Designer: John Bromley
Modeller: John Bromley
Height: 5 ½", 14.0 cm
Colour: Green jacket and skirt; white blouse and underskirt; yellow parasol
Issued: 1988 - 1991
Series: Debutante Collection

Name	U.S. $	Can. $	U.K. £
Sarah Jane	150.00	175.00	85.00

Saturday's Child

Designer: John Bromley
Height: 5 ½", 14.0 cm
Colour: Pale blue and beige
Issued: 1989 - 1991
Series: Children of the Week

Name	U.S. $	Can. $	U.K. £
Saturday's Child	250.00	290.00	145.00

Scarlett

Designer: Shirley Curzon
Modeller: Martin Evans
Height: 8", 20.3 cm
Colour: Red
Issued: 1997 in a limited edition of 2,000
Series: Literary Heroines

Name	U.S. $	Can. $	U.K. £
Scarlett	300.00	425.00	150.00

School Days

Designer: Pauline Shone
Height: 10 ¼" , 26.0 cm
Colour: Pale blue, lilac and white
Issued: 1979 - unknown
Series: Children Studies

Name	U.S. $	Can. $	U.K. £
School Days	340.00	400.00	195.00

Note: Original issue price £75.75.

Secrets

Designer: Pauline Shone
Height: 8 ½", 21.6 cm
Colour: White, beige and pale blue
Issued: 1979 - unknown
Series: Children Studies

Name	U.S. $	Can. $	U.K. £
Secrets	340.00	400.00	195.00

Note: Original issue price £75.75.

Secret Rendezvous

Designer: Elizabeth Greenshields
Modeller: Brian Diment
Height: 8 ¼", 21.0 cm
Colour: Blue and yellow (porcelain)
Issued: 1993 - 1995
Series: Age of Elegance

Name	U.S. $	Can. $	U.K. £
Secret Rendezvous	300.00	425.00	175.00

Selina
Style One

Designer: John Bromley
Height: 3 ½" , 8.9 cm
Colour: Brown
Issued: 1985 - 1988
Varieties: Also called Tricia
Series: Kensington Collection

Name	U.S. $	Can. $	U.K. £
Selina (Style One)	85.00	100.00	50.00

Selina
Style Two

Designer: John Bromley
Modeller: John Bromley
Height: 4 ¾", 12.1 cm
Colour: Purple
Issued: 1991 - 1994
Varieties: Also called Lisa (Style Two)
Series: Debutante Collection

Name	U.S. $	Can. $	U.K. £
Selina (Style Two)	110.00	130.00	65.00

Serenade
Style One

Designer: John Bromley
Modeller: John Bromley
Height: 7", 17.8 cm
Colour: Green dress; yellow underskirt
Issued: 1984 - 1986
Varieties: Also called Jean (Style One); Josephine; Regina; Winsome
Series: Ladies of Fashion

Name	U.S. $	Can. $	U.K. £
Serenade (Style One)	280.00	325.00	160.00

Serenade
Style Two

Designer:	Elizabeth Greenshields
Modeller:	Martin Evans
Height:	8 ¼", 21.0 cm
Colour:	Pale green (porcelain)
Issued:	1991 - 1992
Series:	Age of Elegance

Name	U.S. $	Can. $	U.K. £
Serenade (Style Two)	280.00	325.00	160.00

Serenity

Designer:	Unknown
Height:	8 ½", 21.6 cm
Colour:	Peach dress and hat with red roses
Issued:	1988 - 1991
Series:	Ladies of Fashion

Name	U.S. $	Can. $	U.K. £
Serenity	265.00	300.00	150.00

Sergeant, Cameron Highlanders 1815

Designer:	Unknown
Height:	8 ½", 21.6 cm
Colour:	Red and white tunic; red and blue plaid kilt (matte)
Issued:	1990 in a limited edition of 1,000
Series:	Battle of Waterloo

Name	U.S. $	Can. $	U.K. £
Sergeant, Cameron Highlanders 1815	425.00	500.00	245.00

Sharon
Style One

Designer: John Bromley
Height: 3 ½" , 8.9 cm
Colour: White
Issued: 1985 - 1988
Varieties: Also called Elisa
Series: Kensington Collection

Name	U.S. $	Can. $	U.K. £
Sharon (Style One)	85.00	100.00	50.00

Sharon
Style Two

Designer: Unknown
Modeller: Mike Atkinson
Height: 4 ¾", 12.1 cm
Colour: Peach
Issued: 1997 to the present
Series: Debutante Collection

Name	U.S. $	Can. $	U.K. £
Sharon (Style Two)	100.00	130.00	52.50

Shelley

Designer: John Bromley
Modeller: John Bromley
Height: 5", 12.7 cm
Colour: Pink and lilac dress; white shawl with blue flowers; white hat
Issued: 1986 - 1990
Varieties: Also called Cathy (Style One); Vicki
Series: Debutante Collection

Name	U.S. $	Can. $	U.K. £
Shelley	130.00	150.00	75.00

Shepherd (The)

Designer: Robert Worthington
Height: 8", 20.3 cm
Colour: Brown smock and trousers; green cap; black and white dog
Issued: 1982 - 1985
Series: Character Collection

Name	U.S. $	Can. $	U.K. £
Shepherd (The)	340.00	400.00	195.00

Shepherdess (The)

Designer: John Bromley
Height: 7 ¾", 19.7 cm
Colour: Red and green dress, yellow shawl; white lamb
Issued: 1985 in a limited edition of 1,000
Series: Arcadian Collection

Name	U.S. $	Can. $	U.K. £
Shepherdess	340.00	400.00	195.00

Photograph not available at press time

Ship Ahoy

Designer: David Lyttleton
Height: Unknown
Colour: Unknown
Issued: 1996 in a limited edition of 7,500
Series: Faye Whittaker's Childhood Memories Collection

Name	U.S. $	Can. $	U.K. £
Ship Ahoy	160.00	180.00	90.00

Note: Commissioned by Compton and Woodhouse.

Shirley

Designer:	Unknown
Height:	8 ¼", 21.0 cm
Colour:	Dark and light green
Issued:	1987 - 1991
Series:	Ladies of Fashion

Name	U.S. $	Can. $	U.K. £
Shirley	280.00	320.00	160.00

Shoe Shine Boy (The)

Designer:	Margaret Whittaker
Height:	4 ¼", 10.8 cm
Colour:	Blue suit; black cap; brown shoe box
Issued:	1977 - unknown
Series:	Old London Streets

Name	U.S. $	Can. $	U.K. £
Shoe Shine Boy	300.00	350.00	175.00

Shona

Designer:	Unknown
Modeller:	Adrian Hughes
Height:	8", 20.3 cm
Colour:	Yellow dress; tartan scarf
Issued:	1997 to the present
Series:	Ladies of Fashion

Name	U.S. $	Can. $	U.K. £
Shona	160.00	180.00	89.95

Note: Commissioned by Henderson & Bakers, Scotland.

Shooter (The)
(on wooden plinth)

Designer: John Bromley
Height: 8 ½", 21.6 cm
Colour: Brown
Issued: 1983 - 1984
Series: Sporting Collection

Name	U.S. $	Can. $	U.K. £
Shooter (The)	325.00	375.00	185.00

Sian

Designer: John Bromley
Height: 8", 20.3 cm
Colour: Pale green
Issued: 1996 in a limited edition of 250
Varieties: Also called Stephanie (Style Two)
Series: Welsh Ladies of Fashion

Name	U.S. $	Can. $	U.K. £
Sian	150.00	180.00	89.95

Note: Commissioned by Y Ledi Degan, Llangnefni, Wales.

Silk

Designer: Elizabeth Greenshields
Modeller: John Bromley
Height: 7 ¼", 18.4 cm
Colour: Orange
Issued: 1993 - 1993
Varieties: Also called Chic; Romance (Style Two)
Series: Chantilly Lace

Name	U.S. $	Can. $	U.K. £
Silk	300.00	350.00	175.00

Silken Lady

Designer: Helen Buckley
Modeller: John Bromley
Height: 8 ¼", 21.0 cm
Colour: Pink and blue
Issued: 1991 - 1994
Series: Ladies of Fashion

Name	U.S. $	Can. $	U.K. £
Silken Lady	300.00	425.00	165.00

Silver Bows

Designer: David Shilling
Modeller: John Bromley
Height: 8 ¾", 22.2 cm
Colour: Silver
Issued: 1986 in limited edition of 1,000
Series: Designer Series

Name	U.S. $	Can. $	U.K. £
Silver Bows	600.00	700.00	350.00

Silversmith

Designer: Margaret Whittaker
Height: 7 ¾", 19.7 cm
Colour: Black
Issued: 1974 - c.1980
Series: Craft Figures

Name	U.S. $	Can. $	U.K. £
Silversmith	300.00	350.00	175.00

Sir Don Bradman

Designer: John Bromley
Height: 8 ½", 21.6 cm
Colour: White and green
Issued: 1984 in a limited edition of 1,000

Name	U.S. $	Can. $	U.K. £
Sir Don Bradman	395.00	450.00	225.00

Note: Commissioned exclusively for the Australian market.

Sir Walter Raleigh

Designer: Robert Worthington
Height: 8 ½", 21.6 cm
Colour: Brown and burgundy
Issued: 1977 - unknown

Name	U.S. $	Can. $	U.K. £
Sir Walter Raleigh	395.00	450.00	225.00

Skater (The)

Designer: Maureen Halson
Height: 7", 17.8 cm
Colour: Rose-pink skating outfit trimmed with ermine; brown skating boots; ermine muff
Issued: 1996 in a limited edition of 12,500
Series: Victorian Seasons

Name	U.S. $	Can. $	U.K. £
Skater (The)	175.00	200.00	100.00

Note: Commissioned by Compton and Woodhouse.

Sleepy Head

Designer:	John Bromley
Height:	4 ¾", 12.1 cm
Colour:	Yellow dress; brown teddy bear and rabbit
Issued:	1980 - unknown
Series:	Childrens Studies

Name	U.S. $	Can. $	U.K. £
Sleepy Head	340.00	400.00	195.00

Society Debut

Designer:	Elizabeth Greenshields
Modeller:	Martin Evans
Height:	8", 20.3 cm
Colour:	Cream and brown (porcelain)
Issued:	1991 - 1993
Series:	Age of Elegance

Name	U.S. $	Can. $	U.K. £
Society Debut	285.00	325.00	165.00

Society Reception

Designer:	Helen Buckley
Modeller:	John Bromley
Height:	8 ½", 21.6 cm
Colour:	Peach (porcelain)
Issued:	1997 to the present
Varieties:	Also called Red Rose of Lancashire
Series:	Age of Elegance

Name	U.S. $	Can. $	U.K. £
Society Reception	275.00	325.00	110.00

Soldier (The)

Designer:	John Bromley
Height:	8", 20.3 cm
Colour:	Khaki
Issued:	1984 in a limited edition of 1,500
Series:	King and Country (1940 Period)

Name	U.S. $	Can. $	U.K. £
Soldier (The)	385.00	440.00	220.00

Sophia
Style One

Designer:	John Bromley
Modeller:	John Bromley
Height:	7 ½", 19.1 cm
Colour:	Red
Issued:	1975 - 1977
Varieties:	Also called Anne (Style One); Dianne
Series:	Ladies of Fashion

Name	U.S. $	Can. $	U.K. £
Sophia (Style One)	300.00	350.00	175.00

Sophia
Style Two

Designer:	John Bromley
Modeller:	John Bromley
Height:	5", 12.7 cm
Colour:	Yellow
Issued:	1983 - 1985
Series:	Debutante Collection

Name	U.S. $	Can. $	U.K. £
Sophia (Style Two)	130.00	150.00	75.00

Sophia
Style Three

Designer: Elizabeth Greenshields
Modeller: Unknown
Height: 8", 20.3 cm
Colour: Blue
Issued: 1992 - 1993
Series: West End Girls

Name	U.S. $	Can. $	U.K. £
Sophia (Style Three)	340.00	400.00	195.00

Sophie
Style One

Designer: John Bromley
Modeller: John Bromley
Height: 5", 12.7 cm
Colour: Lemon
Issued: 1983 - 1989
Varieties: Also called June; Justine; Natalie (Style One); Samantha; Tessa
Series: Debutante Collection

Name	U.S. $	Can. $	U.K. £
Sophie (Style One)	130.00	150.00	75.00

Sophie
Style Two

Designer: John Bromley
Modeller: John Bromley
Height: 8 ½", 21.6 cm
Colour: Red jacket and skirt trimmed with ermine
Issued: 1988 - 1991
Varieties: Also called Harmony
Series: Ladies of Fashion

Name	U.S. $	Can. $	U.K. £
Sophie (Style Two)	285.00	325.00	165.00

Sophie
Style Three

Designer: Unknown
Modeller: Martin Evans
Height: 3 ½", 8.9 cm
Colour: Lemon and white
Issued: 1995 - 1997
Series: Minuettes

Name	U.S. $	Can. $	U.K. £
Sophie (Style Three)	65.00	89.50	30.00

Sophie Promenading on the Champs Elysées

Designer: John Bromley
Height: 7 ½", 19.1 cm
Colour: Peach dress with darker peach bows and trim; peach hat; peach parasol with darker peach roses
Issued: 1991 in a limited edition of 12,500
Series: La Belle Epoque

Name	U.S. $	Can. $	U.K. £
Sophie Promenading on the Champs Elysées	265.00	300.00	150.00

Note: Commissioned by Compton and Woodhouse.

Sophisticated Lady (The)

Designer: Helen Buckley
Modeller: John Bromley
Height: 8 ¼", 21.0 cm
Colour: Red
Issued: 1990 - 1997
Series: Ladies of Fashion

Name	U.S. $	Can. $	U.K. £
Sophisticated Lady	325.00	425.00	135.00

Southern Belle

Designer: Helen Buckley
Modeller: John Bromley
Height: 7 ¾", 19.7 cm
Colour: White and pink
Issued: 1986 - 1993
Series: Ladies of Fashion

Name	U.S. $	Can. $	U.K. £
Southern Belle	285.00	325.00	165.00

Spanish Serenade

Designer: Elizabeth Greenshields
Modeller: Brian Diment
Height: 8 ¼", 21.0 cm
Colour: Peach and blue (porcelain)
Issued: 1993 to the present
Series: Age of Elegance

Name	U.S. $	Can. $	U.K. £
Spanish Serenade	300.00	445.00	160.00

Special Anniversary

Designer: David Shilling
Modeller: John Bromley
Height: 8 ¼", 21.0 cm
Colour: Mauve and pink
Issued: 1988 in a limited edition of 1.000
Series: Designer Collection

Name	U.S. $	Can. $	U.K. £
Special Anniversary	650.00	750.00	375.00

Special Day

Designer: John Bromley
Height: 5 ¼", 13.3 cm
Colour: White and cream
Issued: 1991 - 1994
Series: Debutante Collection

Name	U.S. $	Can. $	U.K. £
Special Day	125.00	160.00	95.00

Special Memories

Designer: Helen Buckley
Modeller: John Bromley
Height: 7 ¾", 19.7 cm
Colour: Lilac and yellow
Issued: 1990 - 1994
Varieties: Also called Anna (Style Two)
Series: Ladies of Fashion

Name	U.S. $	Can. $	U.K. £
Special Memories	250.00	290.00	145.00

Special Occasion

Designer: John Bromley
Modeller: John Bromley
Height: 8 ¼", 21.0 cm
Colour: Green
Issued: 1991 - 1994
Series: Ladies of Fashion

Name	U.S. $	Can. $	U.K. £
Special Occasion	250.00	290.00	145.00

Spring Pageant

Designer:	Elizabeth Greenshields
Modeller:	Martin Evans
Height:	8 ¼", 21.0 cm
Colour:	Beige and green (porcelain)
Issued:	1994 to the present
Series:	Age of Elegance

Name	U.S. $	Can. $	U.K. £
Spring Pageant	225.00	270.00	135.00

Spring Song

Designer:	John Bromley
Modeller:	John Bromley
Height:	8", 20.3 cm
Colour:	Pink dress with rose-pink flowers
Issued:	1984 - 1989
Varieties:	Also called Katherine (Style One); Maureen; Rapture; Rosalee
Series:	Ladies of Fashion

Name	U.S. $	Can. $	U.K. £
Spring Song	280.00	325.00	160.00

Springtime
Style One

Designer:	John Bromley
Modeller:	John Bromley
Height:	7 ¾", 19.7 cm
Colour:	Pink and white
Issued:	1981 in a limited edition of 750
Series:	Four Seasons

Name	U.S. $	Can. $	U.K. £
Springtime (Style One)	365.00	490.00	245.00

Springtime
Style Two

Designer: John Bromley
Modeller: John Bromley
Height: 5 ¼", 13.3 cm
Colour: Pink and white
Issued: 1991 - 1993
Series: Debutante Collection

Name	U.S. $	Can. $	U.K. £
Springtime (Style Two)	115.00	130.00	65.00

Squash Racquets

Designer: John Bromley
Height: 6 ¼", 15.9 cm
Colour: White, blue and brown
Issued: 1986 - 1987
Series: Sporting Collection

Name	U.S. $	Can. $	U.K. £
Squash Racquets	340.00	400.00	195.00

Stable Girl (Cleaning Out)

Designer: Pauline Shone
Height: 8 ½", 21.6 cm
Colour: Cream, white and black
Issued: 1979 - unknown
Series: Children Studies

Name	U.S. $	Can. $	U.K. £
Stable Girl (Cleaning Out)	280.00	325.00	160.00

Stella
Style One

Designer: John Bromley
Modeller: John Bromley
Height: 8", 20.3 cm
Colour: Pale green and lilac
Issued: 1979 - 1986
Varieties: Also called Gemma (Style One)
Series: Ladies of Fashion

Name	U.S. $	Can. $	U.K. £
Stella (Style One)	280.00	325.00	160.00

Stella
Style Two

Designer: Elizabeth Greenshields
Modeller: Martin Evans
Height: 5", 12.7 cm
Colour: Green
Issued: 1993 to the present
Series: Debutante Collection

Name	U.S. $	Can. $	U.K. £
Stella (Style Two)	100.00	160.00	52.50

Stephanie
Style One

Designer: John Bromley
Modeller: John Bromley
Height: 8", 20.3 cm
Colour: Yellow
Issued: 1984
Varieties: Also called Lorraine
Series: Ladies of Fashion

Name	U.S. $	Can. $	U.K. £
Stephanie (Style One)	265.00	300.00	150.00

Note: Commissioned by Grattan Home Shopping.

Stephanie
Style Two

Designer:	John Bromley
Modeller:	John Bromley
Height:	8", 20.3 cm
Colour:	Lilac
Issued:	1992 - 1995
Varieties:	Also called Sian
Series:	Ladies of Fashion

Name	U.S. $	Can. $	U.K. £
Stephanie (Style Two)	200.00	275.00	145.00

Strawberry Fayre
Style Two

Designer:	John Bromley
Modeller:	John Bromley
Height:	7 ¼", 18.4 cm
Colour:	Yellow and white
Issued:	1987 - 1991
Series:	Ladies of Fashion

Name	U.S. $	Can. $	U.K. £
Strawberry Fayre (Style Two)	285.00	325.00	165.00

Strawberry Seller (The)

Designer:	John Bromley
Modeller:	John Bromley
Height:	8 ½", 21.6 cm
Colour:	Blue overdress; white underskirt with red roses; basket of strawberries
Issued:	1995 in a limited edition of 9,500
Series:	Cries of London

Name	U.S. $	Can. $	U.K. £
Strawberry Seller (The)	280.00	325.00	160.00

Note: Commissioned by Compton and Woodhouse.

Sue

Designer: John Bromley
Modeller: John Bromley
Height: 7 ¾", 19.7cm
Colour: Red
Issued: 1975 - 1977
Varieties: Also called Clare; Denise
Series: Ladies of Fashion

Name	U.S. $	Can. $	U.K. £
Sue	300.00	350.00	175.00

Suffragette (The)

Designer: Robert Worthington
Height: 8", 20.3 cm
Colour: Brown jacket and skirt; white blouse and sash; black hat with red and yellow flowers
Issued: 1982 - 1985
Series: Character Collection

Name	U.S. $	Can. $	U.K. £
Suffragette (The)	300.00	350.00	175.00

Summer Breeze
Style One

Designer: John Bromley
Modeller: John Bromley
Height: 7 ¾", 19.7 cm
Colour: Green
Issued: 1984 - 1989
Varieties: Also called Christina; Flora (Style One)
Series: Ladies of Fashion

Name	U.S. $	Can. $	U.K. £
Summer Breeze (Style One)	300.00	325.00	175.00

Summer Breeze
Style Two

Designer:	Elizabeth Greenshields
Modeller:	Jack Glynn
Height:	8 ½", 21.6 cm
Colour:	Lavender (porcelain)
Issued:	1994 to the present
Varieties:	Also called Elaine (Style Two); "Name Your Own"
Series:	Age of Elegance

Name	U.S. $	Can. $	U.K. £
Summer Breeze (Style Two)	200.00	260.00	125.00

Summer Daydream

Designer:	Sheila Mitchell
Height:	6", 15.0 cm
Colour:	Pale blue dress; white rabbit
Issued:	1990 in a limited edition of 9,500
Series:	Moments of the Heart

Name	U.S. $	Can. $	U.K. £
Summer Daydream	175.00	200.00	100.00

Note: Commissioned by Compton and Woodhouse.

Summer Days

Designer:	Helen Buckley
Modeller:	John Bromley
Height:	8 ¼", 21.0 cm
Colour:	Green and pink
Issued:	1991 to the present
Series:	Ladies of Fashion

Name	U.S. $	Can. $	U.K. £
Summer Days	225.00	425.00	150.00

Summer Parade

Designer: Elizabeth Greenshields
Modeller: Brian Diment
Height: 8 ¼", 21.0 cm
Colour: Lavender and yellow (porcelain)
Issued: 1993 - 1994
Series: Age of Elegance

Name	U.S. $	Can. $	U.K. £
Summer Parade	315.00	360.00	180.00

Summer Romance

Designer: Helen Buckley
Modeller: John Bromley
Height: 7 ¾", 19.7 cm
Colour: Pink and white
Issued: 1990 - 1996
Series: Ladies of Fashion

Name	U.S. $	Can. $	U.K. £
Summer Romance	225.00	425.00	160.00

Summer Stroll

Designer: Elizabeth Greenshields
Modeller: Jack Glynn
Height: 9", 22.9 cm
Colour: Red and pink
Issued: 1997 in a limited edition of 1,000
Varieties: Also called Vicky
Series: Ladies of Fashion

Name	U.S. $	Can. $	U.K. £
Summer Stroll	215.00	250.00	125.00

Note: Commissioned by Connaught House, Arnold, Nottinghamshire.

Summer's Day

Designer: John Bromley
Modeller: John Bromley
Height: 7 ½", 19.1 cm
Colour: Lady in yellow dress;
Boy in white sailor suit
Issued: 1981 in a limited edition of 750
Series: Four Seasons

Name	U.S. $	Can. $	U.K. £
Summer's Day	425.00	490.00	245.00

Summertime

Designer: Unknown
Height: 3 ¾ , 9.5 cm
Colour: Peach dress
Issued: 1997 - 1997
Varieties: Hannah (StyleTwo); Michelle (Style Three)
Series: Membership Exclusive

Name	U.S. $	Can. $	U.K. £
Summertime	50.00	60.00	30.00

Sunday Best
Style One

Designer: John Bromley
Modeller: John Bromley
Height: 8 ¼", 21.0 cm
Colour: Red and pink
Issued: 1989 - 1993
Series: Ladies of Fashion

Name	U.S. $	Can. $	U.K. £
Sunday Best (Style One)	280.00	325.00	160.00

Sunday Best
Style Two

Designer: David Lyttleton
Modeller: David Lyttleton
Height: Unknown
Colour: Pink dress with rose-pink polka dots; rose-pink sash; white bonnet; brown teddy bear
Issued: 1996 in a limited edition of 7,500
Series: Faye Whittaker's Childhood Memories Collection

Name	U.S. $	Can. $	U.K. £
Sunday Best (Style Two)	160.00	180.00	90.00

Note: Commissioned by Compton and Woodhouse.

Sunday's Child

Designer: John Bromley
Modeller: John Bromley
Height: 6 ¾" , 17.2 cm
Colour: Pale blue and pink
Issued: 1989 - 1991
Series: Children of the Week

Name	U.S. $	Can. $	U.K. £
Sunday's Child	250.00	290.00	145.00

Surprise Celebration

Designer: David Shilling
Modeller: John Bromley
Height: 8 ¼", 21.0 cm
Colour: White dress with gold highlights; peach stole
Issued: 1988 in a limited edition of 1,000
Series: Designer Series

Name	U.S. $	Can. $	U.K. £
Surprise Celebration	600.00	700.00	350.00

Susan
Style One

Designer: John Bromley
Modeller: John Bromley
Height: 5", 12.7 cm
Colour: Black and white
Issued: 1983 - 1986
Varieties: Also called Andrea; Claire (Style One); Maxine; Pamela (Style One)
Series: Debutante Collection

Name	U.S. $	Can. $	U.K. £
Susan (Style One)	165.00	190.00	95.00

Susan
Style Two

Designer: Helen Buckley
Modeller: Martin Evans
Height: 7 ¾", 19.7 cm
Colour: Pale pink and pale blue
Issued: 1994 to the present
Series: Ladies of Fashion

Name	U.S. $	Can. $	U.K. £
Susan (Style Two)	275.00	325.00	130.00

Suzannah

Designer: Graham Miller
Modeller: Unknown
Height: 10", 25.4 cm
Colour: Pale blue
Issued: 1993 - 1997
Varieties: Also called Kay
Series: Silhouettes

Name	U.S. $	Can. $	U.K. £
Susannah	125.00	235.00	72.50

Sweet Juliet

Designer: John Bromley
Modeller: John Bromley
Height: 9 ½", 24.0 cm
Colour: Yellow and peach
Issued: 1991 in a limited edition of 1,000
Series: English Rose

Name	U.S. $	Can. $	U.K. £
Sweet Juliet	1,400.00	1,600.00	800.00

Sweet 16

Designer: Unknown
Modeller: John Bromley
Height: 5", 12.7 cm
Colour: Blue and pink
Issued: 1992 - 1997
Series: Debutante Collection

Name	U.S. $	Can. $	U.K. £
Sweet 16	100.00	150.00	52.50

Sweetest Rose (The)
Style One

Designer: Sheila Mitchell
Height: 7 ½", 19.1 cm
Colour: White
Issued: 1990 in a limited edition of 9,500
Series: The Ballet Shoes Collection

Name	U.S. $	Can. $	U.K. £
Sweetest Rose (Style One)	140.00	160.00	80.00

Note: Commissioned by Compton and Woodhouse.

Sweetest Rose
Style Two

Designer: Helen Buckley
Modeller: Jack Glynn
Height: 8", 20.3 cm
Colour: Purple and yellow
Issued: 1997 in a limited edition of 2,000
Series: Flower Ladies

Name	U.S. $	Can. $	U.K. £
Sweetest Rose (Style Two)	300.00	495.00	160.00

Sweetheart

Designer: Unknown
Modeller: John Bromley
Height: 5 ½", 14.0 cm
Colour: Pink
Issued: 1995 - 1995
Series: Valentine Debutante of the Year

Name	U.S. $	Can. $	U.K. £
Sweetheart	120.00	160.00	100.00

Taking the Air

Designer: John Bromley
Modeller: John Bromley
Height: 5", 12.7 cm
Colour: Blue
Issued: 1989 - 1992
Series: Debutante Collection

Name	U.S. $	Can. $	U.K. £
Taking the Air	165.00	190.00	95.00

Tamara

Designer:	Elizabeth Greenshields
Modeller:	Martin Evans
Height:	5 ¼", 13.3 cm
Colour:	Peach, green and yellow (porcelain)
Issued:	1993 - 1994
Series:	Beau Monde

Name	U.S. $	Can. $	U.K. £
Tamara	175.00	235.00	95.00

Tapestry

Designer:	Elizabeth Greenshields
Modeller:	Brian Diment
Height:	8 ¼", 21.0 cm
Colour:	Pink and green (porcelain)
Issued:	1993 - 1995
Series:	Age of Elegance

Name	U.S. $	Can. $	U.K. £
Tapestry	300.00	395.00	175.00

Tara

Designer:	John Bromley
Modeller:	John Bromley
Height:	8", 20.3 cm
Colour:	Pink and yellow
Issued:	1987 - 1989
Varieties:	Also called Lynne (Style One)
Series:	Ladies of Fashion

Name	U.S. $	Can. $	U.K. £
Tara	300.00	350.00	175.00

Tea Dance

Designer: Elizabeth Greenshields
Modeller: Brian Diment
Height: 8 ¼", 21.0 cm
Colour: Peach (porcelain)
Issued: 1992 - 1994
Series: Age of Elegance

Name	U.S. $	Can. $	U.K. £
Tea Dance	300.00	350.00	175.00

Tenderness (The)

Designer: John Bromley
Height: 8 ½", 21.6 cm
Colour: Yellow, pink and white
Issued: 1980 - 1982
Series: Ladies of Fashion

Name	U.S. $	Can. $	U.K. £
Tenderness (The)	395.00	450.00	225.00

Tender Thoughts

Designer: Helen Buckley
Modeller: John Bromley
Height: 7 ¾", 19.7 cm
Colour: Lavender and blue
Issued: 1990 - 1994
Series: Ladies of Fashion

Name	U.S. $	Can. $	U.K. £
Tender Thoughts	285.00	325.00	165.00

Tennis Party (The)

Designer:	Unknown
Modeller:	Jenny Oliver
Height:	5", 12.7 cm
Colour:	Lemon and blue
Issued:	1997 in a limited edition of 500
Series:	Wimbledon Collection

Name	U.S. $	Can. $	U.K. £
Tennis Party (The)	95.00	110.00	55.00

Note: Commissioned by China Carousel.

Tennis Player, c.1914

Designer:	Mary Roberts
Modeller:	John Bromley
Height:	8", 20.3 cm
Colour:	Green
Issued:	1986 in a limited edition of 500
Series:	Early Days

Name	U.S. $	Can. $	U.K. £
Tennis Player, c.1914	475..00	550.00	275.00

Note: Commissioned for the Australian market.

Teresa

Designer:	John Bromley
Modeller:	John Bromley
Height:	7 ½", 19.1 cm
Colour:	Yellow - orange
Issued:	1977 - 1990
Varieties:	Also called Amanda (Style One); Anna (Style One); Captivation; Vanity Fayre
Series:	Ladies of Fashion

Name	U.S. $	Can. $	U.K. £
Teresa	250.00	290.00	145.00

Tess

Designer: John Bromley
Modeller: John Bromley
Height: 8", 20.3 cm
Colour: White and gold
Issued: 1991 - 1993
Varieties: Also called Young Love
Series: Grosvenor Collection

Name	U.S. $	Can. $	U.K. £
Tess	250.00	290.00	145.00

Tessa

Designer: John Bromley
Modeller: John Bromley
Height: 5", 12.7 cm
Colour: Blue
Issued: 1985
Varieties: Also called June; Justine; Natalie (Style One); Samantha; Sophie (Style One)
Series: Debutante Collection

Name	U.S. $	Can. $	U.K. £
Tessa	140.00	160.00	80.00

Note: Commissioned by Grattan Home Shopping.

Thank You

Designer: John Bromley
Modeller: John Bromley
Height: 5", 12.7 cm
Colour: Lavender and pink
Issued: 1992 to the present
Series: Debutante Collection

Name	U.S. $	Can. $	U.K. £
Thank You	100.00	150.00	52.50

Thoughts

Designer:	John Bromley
Height:	7 ¾", 19.7 cm
Colour:	Green dress with yellow underskirt
Issued:	1979 - 1982
Series:	Ladies of Fashion

Name	U.S. $	Can. $	U.K. £
Thoughts	285.00	325.00	165.00

Thursday's Child

Designer:	John Bromley
Height:	7 ¼", 18.4 cm
Colour:	Blue and brown
Issued:	1989 - 1991
Series:	Children of the Week

Name	U.S. $	Can. $	U.K. £
Thursday's Child	250.00	290.00	145.00

Tina

Designer:	John Bromley
Height:	6 ½", 16.5 cm
Colour:	Lavender
Issued:	1985
Varieties:	Also called Kelly
Series:	Ladies of Fashion

Name	U.S. $	Can. $	U.K. £
Tina	285.00	325.00	165.00

Note: Commissioned by Grattan Home Shopping.

Tom Sawyer

Designer: John Bromley
Height: 8 ¾", 22.2 cm
Colour: Beige shirt, blue dungarees, brown barrel
Issued: 1981 in a limited edition of 2,500

Name	U.S. $	Can. $	U.K. £
Tom Sawyer	300.00	350.00	175.00

Note: Commissioned by Canadian Collector Plates, Milliken, Ontario.

Topaz

Designer: Maureen Halson
Height: 9 ¼", 23.5 cm
Colour: Light to dark amber dress; lilac flowers; gold trimmings
Issued: 1993 in a limited edition of 9,500
Series: Spirits of the Jewels

Name	U.S. $	Can. $	U.K. £
Topaz	280.00	325.00	160.00

Note: Commissioned by Compton and Woodhouse.

Tower of London Beefeater

Designer: Margaret Whittaker
Height: 9", 22.9 cm
Colour: Black and red
Issued: 1981 - 1985
Series: London Heritage

Name	U.S. $	Can. $	U.K. £
Tower of London Beefeater	300.00	350.00	175.00

Town Crier (The)
Designer: Robert Worthington
Height: 9 ¼", 23.5 cm
Colour: Dark blue, red and white
Issued: Unknown, in a limited edition of 1,000

Name	U.S. $	Can. $	U.K. £
Town Crier (The)	300.00	350.00	175.00

Tracy
Designer: John Bromley
Modeller: John Bromley
Height: 5", 12.7 cm
Colour: Pink
Issued: 1983 - 1989
Varieties: Also called Gwen; Jill (Style One); Mary (Style One); Vivienne
Series: Debutante Collection

Name	U.S. $	Can. $	U.K. £
Tracy	165.00	190.00	95.00

Tricia
Designer: John Bromley
Modeller: John Bromley
Height: 3 ½", 8.9 cm
Colour: Pale blue
Issued: 1985 - 1988
Varieties: Also called Selina (Style One)
Series: Kensington Collection

Name	U.S. $	Can. $	U.K. £
Tricia	85.00	100.00	50.00

Trooper, 2nd Dragoons 1815

Designer:	Unknown
Height:	8 ½", 21.6 cm
Colour:	Red and gold tunic; blue and beige trousers (porcelain)
Issued:	1990 in a limited edition of 1,000
Series:	Battle of Waterloo Collection

Name	U.S. $	Can. $	U.K. £
Trooper, 2nd Dragoons 1815	475.00	550.00	275.00

True Love

Designer:	Elizabeth Greenshields
Modeller:	Unknown
Height:	5", 12.7 cm
Colour:	Yellow and pink
Issued:	1992 to the present
Series:	Debutante Collection

Name	U.S. $	Can. $	U.K. £
True Love	100.00	150.00	52.50

Tuesday's Child

Designer:	John Bromley
Height:	6 ¾", 17.2 cm
Colour:	Blue and pink
Issued:	1989 - 1991
Series:	Children of the Week

Name	U.S. $	Can. $	U.K. £
Tuesday's Child	250.00	290.00	145.00

Tutankhamun

Designer: John Bromley
Height: 7", 17.8 cm
Colour: Gold and blue
Issued: 1975 in a limited edition of 250
Series: Egyptian Busts

Name	U.S. $	Can. $	U.K. £
Tutankhamun	525.00	600.00	300.00

Twenties Party

Designer: David Shilling
Modeller: John Bromley
Height: 8 ¾", 22.2 cm
Colour: Mauve
Issued: 1987 in a limited edition of 1,000
Series: Designer Series

Name	U.S. $	Can. $	U.K. £
Twenties Party	650.00	750.00	375.00

Twenty-One Today

Designer: Elizabeth Greenshields
Modeller: John Bromley
Height: 8", 20.3 cm
Colour: Pale green and pale pink
Issued: 1992 to the present
Series: Ladies of Fashion

Name	U.S. $	Can. $	U.K. £
Twenty-One Today	200.00	330.00	125.00

Ursula

Designer: John Bromley
Modeller: John Bromley
Height: 8 ½", 21.6 cm
Colour: Red and white
Issued: 1985 - 1988
Series: Ladies of Fashion

Name	U.S. $	Can. $	U.K. £
Ursula	285.00	325.00	165.00

Valerie

Designer: Helen Buckley
Modeller: John Bromley
Height: 8", 20.3 cm
Colour: Red
Issued: 1996 to the present
Series: Ladies of Fashion

Name	U.S. $	Can. $	U.K. £
Valerie	250.00	325.00	110.00

Vanessa
Style One

Designer: John Bromley
Modeller: John Bromley
Height: 8 ¼", 21.0 cm
Colour: Yellow and green
Issued: 1978 - 1982
Series: Ladies of Fashion

Name	U.S. $	Can. $	U.K. £
Vanessa (Style One)	300.00	350.00	175.00

Vanessa
Style Two

Designer: John Bromley
Modeller: John Bromley
Height: 8", 20.3 cm
Colour: Yellow and white
Issued: 1997 to the present
Series: Ladies of Fashion

Name	U.S. $	Can. $	U.K. £
Vanessa (Style Two)	175.00	200.00	100.00

Note: Commissioned by Littlewoods Home Shopping.

Vanity Fayre

Designer: John Bromley
Modeller: John Bromley
Height: 7 ½", 19.1 cm
Colour: Green
Issued: 1984 - 1986
Varieties: Also called Amanda (Style One); Anna (Style One); Captivation; Teresa
Series: Ladies of Fashion

Name	U.S. $	Can. $	U.K. £
Vanity Fayre	300.00	350.00	175.00

Velvet

Designer: Elizabeth Greenshields
Modeller: John Bromley
Height: 7 ¼", 18.4 cm
Colour: Peach
Issued: 1992 - 1993
Varieties: Also called Pearl
Series: Chantilly Lace

Name	U.S. $	Can. $	U.K. £
Velvet	325.00	285.00	165.00

Photograph not available at press time

Verity

Designer:	John Bromley
Height:	9", 22.9 cm
Clothing:	Unknown
Issued:	1987 - 1988
Series:	Somerset Collection

Name	U.S. $	Can. $	U.K. £
Verity	285.00	325.00	165.00

Note: Verity is a porcelain figurine dressed in hand-sewn clothing. Prices are for figurine in mint condition with original clothing.

Veronica
Style One

Designer:	John Bromley
Modeller:	John Bromley
Height:	5", 12.7 cm
Colour:	Pale green
Issued:	1984 - 1988
Varieties:	Also called Kimberley (Style One); Lydia (Style One)
Series:	Debutante Collection

Name	U.S. $	Can. $	U.K. £
Veronica (Style One)	165.00	190.00	90.00

Veronica
Style Two

Designer:	John Bromley
Modeller:	John Bromley
Height:	8 ½", 21.6 cm
Colour:	Lilac
Issued:	1992 to the present
Series:	Ladies of Fashion

Name	U.S. $	Can. $	U.K. £
Veronica (Style Two)	150.00	275.00	110.00

Veronica
Style Three

Designer: Jack Glynn
Height: 3 ½", 8.9 cm
Colour: Blue overdress; blue flowers on pale blue underskirt; basket of flowers; gold trimming
Issued: 1993 in a limited edition of 15,000
Series: Fairest Flowers

Name	U.S. $	Can. $	U.K. £
Veronica (Style Three)	125.00	150.00	70.00

Note: Commissioned by Compton and Woodhouse.

Vicki

Designer: John Bromley
Modeller: John Bromley
Height: 5", 12.7 cm
Colour: Blue dress; pink scarf
Issued: 1986 - 1990
Varieties: Also called Cathy (Style One); Shelley
Series: Debutante Collection

Name	U.S. $	Can. $	U.K. £
Vicki	130.00	150.00	75.00

Vicky

Designer: Elizabeth Greenshields
Modeller: Jack Glynn
Height: 9", 22.9 cm
Colour: Lemon and peach
Issued: 1994 to the present
Varieties: Also called Summer Stroll
Series: Ladies of Fashion

Name	U.S. $	Can. $	U.K. £
Vicky	250.00	355.00	145.00

Victoria
Style One

Designer: John Bromley
Modeller: John Bromley
Height: 8 ¼", 21.0 cm
Colour: Pink
Issued: 1975 - 1979
Varieties: Also called Eileen; Emma (Style One); Frances; The Hostess
Series: Ladies of Fashion

Name	U.S. $	Can. $	U.K. £
Victoria (Style One)	285.00	325.00	165.00

Victoria
Style Two

Designer: John Bromley
Modeller: John Bromley
Height: 7 ¾", 19.7 cm
Colour: Dark and pale green
Issued: 1984
Varieties: Also called Cheryl
Series: Ladies of Fashion

Name	U.S. $	Can. $	U.K. £
Victoria (Style Two)	285.00	325.00	165.00

Note: Commissioned by Grattan Home Shopping.

Victoria
Style Three

Designer: Helen Buckley
Modeller: Andy Moss
Height: 5 ¼", 13.3 cm
Colour: Pale blue and pale yellow (porcelain)
Issued: 1997 to the present
Series: Beau Monde

Name	U.S. $	Can. $	U.K. £
Victoria (Style Three)	100.00	155.00	57.50

Victoria Gardens

Designer: John Bromley
Modeller: John Bromley
Height: 7 ¼", 18.4 cm
Colour: Pale green and cream (porcelain)
Issued: 1995 - 1997
Series: Age of Elegance

Name	U.S. $	Can. $	U.K. £
Victoria Gardens	200.00	270.00	120.00

Vienna

Designer: Caroline Holmes
Modeller: Jack Glynn
Height: 10", 25.4 cm
Colour: Shaded buttermilk and mother of pearl lustre
Issued: 1997 in a limited edition of 2,000
Series: Modern Brides Collection

Name	U.S. $	Can. $	U.K. £
Vienna	350.00	495.00	175.00

Violet
Style One

Designer: Unknown
Height: 5", 12.7 cm
Colour: Lavender and mauve
Issued: 1993 - 1997
Varieties: Also called Endless Love
Series: Debutante Collection

Name	U.S. $	Can. $	U.K. £
Violet (Style One)	100.00	150.00	52.50

Violet
Style Two

Designer: Jack Glynn
Height: 3 ½", 8.9 cm
Colour: Dark and light purple overdress; white underskirt with purple flowers; gold trim
Issued: 1993 in a limited edition of 15,000
Series: Fairest Flowers

Name	U.S. $	Can. $	U.K. £
Violet (Style Two)	125.00	140.00	69.00

Note: Commissioned by Compton and Woodhouse.

Virginia

Designer: Helen Buckley
Modeller: John Bromley
Height: 9", 22.9 cm
Clothing: Dark green silk dress and hat trimmed with lace; lace parasol
Issued: 1985 - 1988
Series: Somerset Collection

Name	U.S. $	Can. $	U.K. £
Virginia	300.00	350.00	175.00

Note: Virginia is a porcelain figurine dressed in hand-sewn clothing. Prices are for figurine in mint condition with original clothing.

Photograph not available at press time

Visiting Day (Boy)

Designer: Elizabeth Woodhouse
Modeller: Sheila Mitchell
Height: 7 ¾", 19.7 cm
Colour: Unknown
Issued: 1986 in a limited edition of 9,500

Name	U.S. $	Can. $	U.K. £
Visiting Day (Boy)	300.00	350.00	175.00

Note: Commissioned by Compton and Woodhouse and issued to commemorate 100 years of the Hospital for Sick Children, Great Ormond Street, London.

Visiting Day (Girl)

Designer: Elizabeth Woodhouse
Modeller: Sheila Mitchell
Height: 7 ¾", 19.7 cm
Colour: Pale blue dress and shawl; white apron
Issued: 1986 in a limited edition of 9,500

Name	U.S. $	Can. $	U.K. £
Visiting Day (Girl)	300.00	350.00	175.00

Note: Commissioned by Compton and Woodhouse and issued to commemorate 100 years of the Hospital for Sick Children, Great Ormond Street, London.

Vivien

Designer: Elizabeth Greenshields
Modeller: Unknown
Height: 8 ¼", 21.0 cm
Colour: Green
Issued: 1992 - 1993
Series: West End Girls

Name	U.S. $	Can. $	U.K. £
Vivien	385.00	440.00	220.00

Vivienne

Designer: John Bromley
Modeller: John Bromley
Height: 5", 12.7 cm
Colour: Blue
Issued: 1983 - 1985
Varieties: Also called Gwen; Jill (Style One); Mary (Style One); Tracy
Series: Debutante Collection

Name	U.S. $	Can. $	U.K. £
Vivienne	175.00	200.00	100.00

Wakefield Rose

Designer:	Unknown
Height:	8 ½", 21.6 cm
Colour:	Blue dress with darker blue trim; white hat with dark blue ribbon
Issued:	1996 in a limited edition of 200
Varieties:	Also called Kathleen
Series:	Ladies of Fashion

Name	U.S. $	Can. $	U.K. £
Wakefield Rose	175.00	200.00	99.95

Note: Commissioned by Peter Jones China Ltd., Wakefield.

Water

Designer:	Sue Cashmore
Modeller:	John Bromley
Height:	9 ½", 24.0 cm
Colour:	Blue
Issued:	1989 in a limited edition of 1,000
Series:	The Elements

Name	U.S. $	Can. $	U.K. £
Water	450.00	500.00	250.00

Wedding Bells

Designer:	Elizabeth Greenshields
Modeller:	John Bromley
Height:	9 ½", 24.0 cm
Colour:	White dress with lilac shaggy flowers; gold highlights
Issued:	1994 - 1994
Series:	Bride of the Year

Name	U.S. $	Can. $	U.K. £
Wedding Bells	400.00	650.00	295.00

Wedding Day

Designer: John Bromley and Douglas Tootle
Height: 8 ¼", 21.0 cm
Colour: White and pink
Issued: 1989 - 1992
Varieties: Also called Romantic Bride
Series: Brides

Name	U.S. $	Can. $	U.K. £
Wedding Day	340.00	400.00	195.00

Wednesday's Child

Designer: John Bromley
Height: 4 ¾", 12.1 cm
Colour: Blue and beige
Issued: 1989 - 1991
Series: Children of the Week

Name	U.S. $	Can. $	U.K. £
Wednesday's Child	300.00	350.00	175.00

Wendy

Designer: Unknown
Height: 7 ½", 19.1 cm
Colour: Yellow
Issued: 1979 - 1988
Series: Ladies of Fashion

Name	U.S. $	Can. $	U.K. £
Wendy	300.00	350.00	175.00

White Faced Serenade

Designer: John Bromley
Height: 9", 22.0 cm
Colour: White, blue, red and yellow
Issued: 1985 - 1988
Series: Cavalcade of Clowns

Name	U.S. $	Can. $	U.K. £
White Faced Serenade	325.00	375.00	185.00

White Rose of Yorkshire

Designer: John Bromley
Modeller: John Bromley
Height: 8 ½", 21.6 cm
Colour: Red
Issued: 1996 in a limited edition of 500
Varieties: Also called Matinee Performance
Series: Ladies of Fashion

Name	U.S. $	Can. $	U.K. £
White Rose of Yorkshire	175.00	200.00	99.95

Note: Commissioned by Peter Jones China Ltd., Wakefield.

Whitehall Lifeguard

Designer: Margaret Whittaker
Height: 10 ½", 26.7 cm
Colour: Red, silver, white and black
Issued: 1980 - 1985
Series: London Heritage

Name	U.S. $	Can. $	U.K. £
Whitehall Lifeguard	325.00	375.00	185.00

Wig Maker

Designer: Margaret Whittaker
Height: 8 ¼", 21.0 cm
Colour: Brown
Issued: 1979 - c.1980
Series: Craft Figures

Name	U.S. $	Can. $	U.K. £
Wig Maker	300.00	350.00	175.00

William the Gangster

Designer: Catherine Barnsley
Height: Unknown
Colour: Blue
Issued: 1977 - c.1980
Series: Just William

Name	U.S. $	Can. $	U.K. £
William the Gangster	300.00	350.00	175.00

William Shakespeare
Style One

Designer: Robert Worthington
Height: 8 ½", 21.6 cm
Colour: Dark brown waistcoat; white shirt; tan breeches; green cloak
Issued: 1979 - 1982
Series: Characters from Shakespeare

Name	U.S. $	Can. $	U.K. £
William Shakespeare (Style One)	475.00	550.00	275.00

William Shakespeare
Style Two

Designer: Unknown
Height: 9", 22.0 cm
Colour: Dark brown waistcoat; white shirt; tan breeches; black cloak
Issued: 1981 - 1982
Series: Characters from Shakespeare

Name	U.S. $	Can. $	U.K. £
William Shakespeare (Style Two)	475.00	550.00	275.00

Winning Stroke

Designer: David Shilling
Modeller: John Bromley
Height: 8 ½", 21.6 cm
Colour: Pale and rose pink
Issued: 1989 in a limited edition of 1,000
Series: Romance of Henley

Name	U.S. $	Can. $	U.K. £
Winning Stroke	600.00	700.00	350.00

Winsome

Designer: John Bromley
Modeller: John Bromley
Height: 7", 17.8 cm
Colour: Rose-pink dress and hat; white and yellow underskirt
Issued: 1984 - 1989
Varieties: Also called Jean (Style One); Josephine; Regina; Serenade (Style One)
Series: Ladies of Fashion

Name	U.S. $	Can. $	U.K. £
Winsome	285.00	325.00	165.00

Winter Frolic

Designer:	John Bromley
Height:	6 ½", 16.5 cm
Colour:	Girl - Pink and white; Boy - Grey
Issued:	1982 in a limited edition of 750
Series:	Four Seasons

Name	U.S. $	Can. $	U.K. £
Winter Frolic	475.00	550.00	275.00

Winter Slopes (on wooden plinth)

Designer:	John Bromley
Height:	8", 20.3 cm
Colour:	Black, lilac and red
Issued:	1984 - 1987
Series:	Sporting Collection

Name	U.S. $	Can. $	U.K. £
Winter Slopes	385.00	440.00	220.00

Winter Stroll

Designer:	John Bromley
Modeller:	John Bromley
Height:	8 ¼", 21.0 cm
Colour:	Pale blue dress; dark green hat and scarf
Issued:	1988 - 1993
Series:	Ladies of Fashion

Name	U.S. $	Can. $	U.K. £
Winter Stroll	250.00	290.00	145.00

Winter's Day (A)

Designer: Unknown
Height: 10 ¾", 27.8 cm
Colour: 1. Red coat
2. Brown coat
Issued: c.1976 - unknown

Colourway	U.S. $	Can. $	U.K. £
1. Red coat	385.00	440.00	220.00
2. Brown coat	385.00	440.00	220.00

Winter's Morn

Designer: John Bromley
Modeller: John Bromley
Height: 8 ¼", 21.0 cm
Colour: Red dress; black cape
Issued: 1988 - 1990
Varieties: Also called Colleen
Series: Ladies of Fashion

Name	U.S. $	Can. $	U.K. £
Winter's Morn	300.00	350.00	175.00

Woeful Tramp

Designer: John Bromley
Height: 7 ¾", 19.7 cm
Colour: Green, white, blue and red
Issued: 1985 - 1988
Series: Cavalcade of Clowns

Name	U.S. $	Can. $	U.K. £
Woeful Tramp	340.00	400.00	195.00

Woodcutter (The)

Designer: John Bromley
Height: 8", 20.3 cm
Colour: Green, cream and orange
Issued: 1984 in a limited edition of 1,000
Series: Arcadian Collection

Name	U.S. $	Can. $	U.K. £
Woodcutter (The)	340.00	400.00	195.00

Yasmin

Designer: John Bromley
Modeller: John Bromley
Height: 8 ½", 21.6 cm
Colour: Lavender
Issued: 1992 - 1994
Series: Ladies of Fashion

Name	U.S. $	Can. $	U.K. £
Yasmin	285.00	325.00	165.00

Young Love

Designer: John Bromley
Modeller: John Bromley
Height: 8", 20.3 cm
Colour: White and pink
Issued: 1988 - 1996
Varieties: Also called Tess
Series: Ladies of Fashion

Name	U.S. $	Can. $	U.K. £
Young Love	285.00	350.00	160.00

Young Victoria

Designer: John Bromley
Height: 8", 20.3 cm
Colour: Pink
Issued: 1980 - 1982

Name	U.S. $	Can. $	U.K. £
Young Victoria	675.00	800.00	395.00

Yum Yum

Designer: Unknown
Height: Unknown
Colour: Unknown
Issued: 1979 - 1981
Series: Gilbert and Sullivan

Name	U.S. $	Can. $	U.K. £
Yum Yum	650.00	750.00	375.00

Photograph not available at press time

Zara

Designer: John Bromley
Modeller: John Bromley
Height: 5", 12.7 cm
Colour: Red
Issued: 1986 - 1989
Varieties: Also called Dee; Lindsay
Series: Debutante Collection

Name	U.S. $	Can. $	U.K. £
Zara	165.00	190.00	95.00

Zelda

Designer: Unknown
Height: 7 ¾", 19.7 cm
Colour: White with gold highlights
Issued: 1991 - 1992
Series: The Roaring Twenties (Style One)

Name	U.S. $	Can. $	U.K. £
Zelda	285.00	325.00	165.00

Zoe
Style One

Designer: John Bromley
Modeller: John Bromley
Height: 3 ¼", 8.3 cm
Colour: Dark and pale green
Issued: 1985 - 1988
Varieties: Also called Kirsty (Style One)
Series: Kensington Collection

Name	U.S. $	Can. $	U.K. £
Zoe (Style One)	85.00	100.00	50.00

Zoe
Style Two

Designer: Unknown
Modeller: Martin Evans
Height: 3 ¾", 9.5 cm
Colour: Pink
Issued: 1995 to the present
Varieties: Also called Holly (Style Three)
Series: Minuettes

Name	U.S. $	Can. $	U.K. £
Zoe (Style Two)	55.00	79.50	30.00

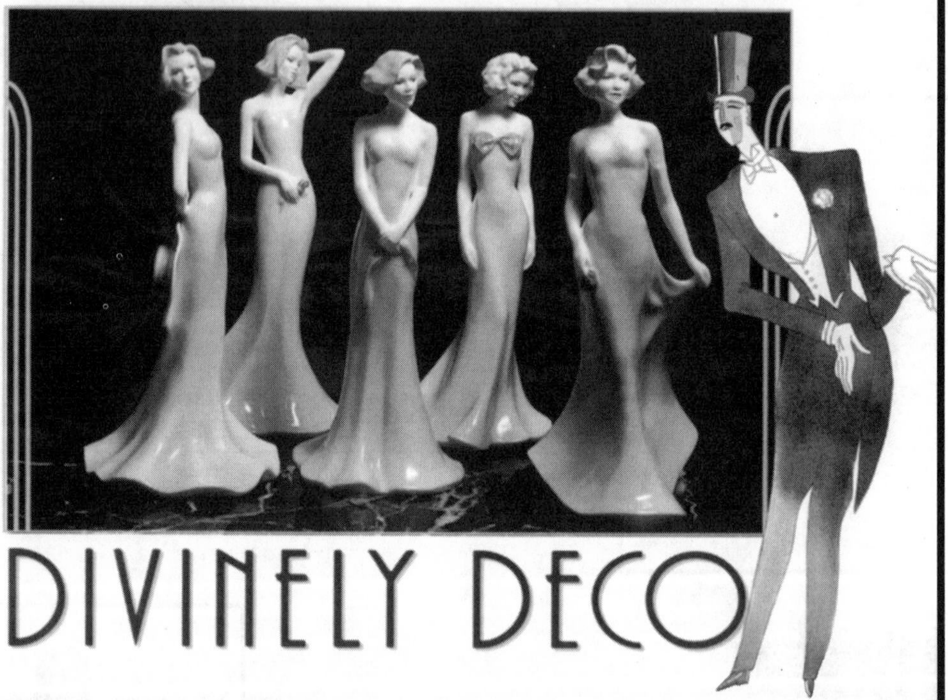

DIVINELY DECO

COLLECTING BY SERIES

Battle of Waterloo Collection

559321

Sergeant, Cameron Highlanders 1815
SIZE: 8·5 ins/22·0 cms

Trooper, 2nd Dragoons 1815
SIZE: 8·5 ins/22·0 cms

Corporal, Royal Horse Artillery 1815
SIZE: 8·5 ins/22·0 cms
LIMITED EDITION OF 1,000 EACH FIGURINE

Officer, 18th Hussars 1814
SIZE: 8·5 ins/22·0 cms

Age of Elegance

Afternoon Matinee
Autumn Stroll
Blenheim Park
Brighton Promenade
Chelsea Reception
Cheyne Walk
Chiswick Walk
Command Performance
Covent Garden
Donna (Style Two)
Easter Bonnet
Esplanade
Evening at the Opera
Gala Occasion
Grand Parade
Hyde Park
Interlude
Lavender Walk
Magnolia Parade
Mandarin Crescent
Martha Rose
Matinee Performance
Midsummer Stroll
Montpellier Walk
Moonlit Rendezvous
On The Balcony
Opening Night
Operetta
Petticoat Lane
Polonaise Walk
Promenade (Style Two)
Regents Park
Rose Crescent
Royal Gala
Secret Rendezvous
Serenade (Style Two)
Society Debut
Society Reception
Spanish Serenade
Spring Pageant
Summer Breeze (Style Two)
Summer Parade
Tapestry
Tea Dance
Victoria Gardens

Age of Elegance Figure of the Year

Evening Promenade, 1995
First Waltz, 1996
Midsummer Dream, 1997

Arcadian Collection

Apple Girl, The
Flower Girl, The (Style Two)
Goose Girl, The (Style One)
Reaper, The
Shepherdess, The
Woodcutter, The

Ascot Ladies

Ascot Lady, 1984, The
Ascot Lady, 1985, The
Ascot Lady, 1986, The
Ascot Lady, 1987, The
Ascot Lady, 1988, The
Ascot Lady, 1989, The

Ballet Shoes Collection, The

Butterflies
Curtain Call
Flower Fairy
Little Swan
Sweetest Rose, The (Style One)

Barnardo's

Christmas Kitten, A
Innocence
Present for Grandma, A

Basia Zarzycka Collection

Lovely Lady Christabel, The
My Dearest Emma

Battle of Waterloo

Corporal, Royal Horse Artillery 1815
Officer, 18th Hussars 1814
Sergeant, Cameron Highlanders 1815
Trooper, 2nd Dragoons 1815

Beau Monde

Alexandra (Style Two)
Anastasia
Angela
Beatrice (Style Two)
Berenice
Charlotte (Style Three)
Christine (Style Three)
Clara
Clarissa (Style Two)
Cordelia
Deborah
Elizabeth (Style Two)
Ellen
Estelle (Style Three)
Francesca (Style Two)
Georgina (Style Two)
Harriet
Isabella (Style Two)
Jill (Style Two)
Kate (Style Two)
Katherine (Style Two)
Laetitia
Laura (Style Two)
Lynne (Style Two)
Madelaine
Molly

Beau Monde (cont.)

Olivia (Style One)
Rachel (Style Two)
Rebecca (Style Three)
Rose (Style Three)
Ruth
Tamara
Victoria (Style Three)

Beau Monde Figure of the Year

Juliette (Style Three), 1997

Bride of The Year

Champagne Reception,1993
Wedding Bells, 1994

Brides

Bride, The (Style Two)
Marie (Style One)
Radiance (Bride)
Romantic Bride
Wedding Day

Cavalcade of Clowns

Auguste's Bouquet
Auguste's Mishap
White Faced Serenade
Woeful Tramp

Celebration of the Season

Lilac Time

Chantilly Lace

Attraction
Breeze (Style Two)
Caress
Charm
Chic
Chloe (Style Two)
Demure
Dignity
Finesse
Glamour
Graceful
High Style
Julia (Style Two)
Lace
Panache
Pearl
Poise
Romance (Style Two)
Silk
Velvet

Character Collection

Apple Woman
Flower Seller (Style Two)
Medicine Man, The
Music Seller, The
News Sheet Seller, The
Pie Maker, The
Poacher, The
Shepherd, The
Suffragette, The

Characters from Shakespeare

Antony
Hamlet
Henry IV
Henry V
Julius Caesar
Malvolio
Mark Antony
Ophelia
Richard II
Romeo and Juliet
William Shakespeare (Style One)
William Shakespeare (Style Two)

Children Studies

Boy Boating
Boy Climbing Tree
Boy Fishing
Bridesmaid (Style Three)
Childhood Days
Feeding Time
Girl with Afghan
Girl with Paddington Bear
Girl with Staffordshire Bull Terrier
Girl with Yorkshire Terrier
I Love Kitty
Little Workman, The
Lucy (Style Two)
Making Up
My Teddy
Repose
Riding Lesson
School Days
Secrets
Sleepy Head
Stable Girl

Children of the Week

Friday's Child
Monday's Child
Saturday's Child
Sunday's Child
Thursday's Child
Tuesday's Child
Wednesday's Child

Christmas Collection

Christmas Angel
Christmas Caroller
Christmas Glee

Coalport Heirloom Figurine of the Year

Olivia (Style Three), 1997

Collingwood Collection

Catherine (Style Two)
Claire (Style Two)
Mary (Style Two)

Craft Figures

Basket Maker, The
Blacksmith, The
Cobbler, The
Saddler, The
Silversmith
Wig Maker

Cries of London

Cherry Seller, The
Flower Seller (Style Three)
Lavender Seller, The
Milk Maid
Oranges and Lemons
Strawberry Seller, The

Dancing Years

Elegant Fifties, The
Elegant Eighties, The
Gay Nineties, The
Romantic Seventies, The

Debutante Collection

Amanda (Style Two)
Amy (Style Two)
Andrea
Anita
Ann
Annette (Style Four)
April
Beatrice (Style One)
Becky
Beth
Bonnie Lass
Carla
Caroline (Style Two)
Carrie
Cassie
Cathy
Catriona
Celebration Time
Chelsea
Christine (Style Two)
Claire (Style One)
Claudette (Style Two)
Congratulations
Danielle (Style Two)
Dawn (Style Two)
Dee
Elaine (Style One)
Eleanor (Style One)
Eloise
Emma Louise
Encore

Debutante Collection (cont.)

Estelle (Style Two)
Fascination
Fiona (Style Two)
Fiona (Style Three)
Garden Party, The
Giselle (Style Two)
Grace (Style One)
Gwen
Hannah (Style One)
In Love
In Vogue
Jacqueline (Style One)
Jane (Style Two)
Janice
Jayne (Style Two)
Jeanette (Style Two)
Jennifer (Style Two)
Jill (Style One)
Jo
Joanne (Style One)
Juliette (Style Two)
June (Style Two)
June (Style Three)
Justine
Karen (Style One)
Katie
Kerry
Kimberley (Style One)
Kirsty (Style Two)
Lauren (Style Two)
Lesley (Style Two)
Lindsay
Lisa (Style Two)
Loretta
Lorna
Love Token
Lucinda (Style Two)
Lucy (Style Three)
Lydia (Style One)
Lynette (Style Two)
Marie (Style Two)
Mary (Style One)
Maxine
May Ball
Melanie (Style Two)
Meryl
Michelle (Style Two)
Millie (Style One)
Mirinda
Nanette (Style Two)
Natalie (Style One)
Nicolette (Style Two)
Nina
Pamela (Style One)
Party Time
Paulette (Style Two)
Penelope (Style Two)
Penny
Poppy (Style One)
Prudence
Rosamund
Rose Marie
Rosie (Style One)
Samantha
Sandra

Debutante Collection (cont.)

Sarah Jane
Selina (Style Two)
Sharon (Style Two)
Shelley
Sophia (Style Two)
Sophie (Style One)
Special Day
Springtime (Style Two)
Stella (Style Two)
Susan (Style One)
Sweet Sixteen
Taking The Air
Tessa
Thank You
Tracy
True Love
Veronica (Style One)
Vicki
Violet (Style One)
Vivienne
Zara

Debutante of the Year

Cinderella's Ball, 1996
Opera at Glyndebourne, 1994
Poppy Ball, 1997
Queen Charlotte's Ball, 1992
Rose Ball, 1995
Royal Caledonian Ball, 1993

Designer Series

Bedtime Story
Dinner at 8
Foxy Lady
L.A. Gala
Night at the Opera
Rendezvous in Rio
Silver Bows
Special Anniversary
Surprise Celebration
Twenties Party

Early Days

Croquet Game, The
Lady with Dog, c.1810
Tennis Player, c.1914

Edwardian Beauties

Angelica
Edwina
Francesca (Style One)
Isabella (Style One)
Philomena
Rebecca (Style Two)

Edwardian Garden Party

Lady Caroline at The Summer Garden Party

Egyptian Busts

Nefertiti
Tutankhamun

Elegant Edwardians

Meeting at Ascot, A

The Elements

Air
Earth
Fire
Water

Empress Collection

Catherine The Great of Russia

English Rose

Blue Moon
English Elegance
Lady Sylvia
Marlena
May Queen
Moonlight
Pretty Jessica
Sweet Juliet

Fabled Beauties

Cleopatra
Delilah
Helen of Troy
Queen of Sheba
Salome

Fairest Flowers

Daisy (Style Two)
Daphne (Style Two)
Flora (Style Two)
Fuchsia
Heather (Style Three)
Holly (Style Two)
Hyacinth
Iris (Style One)
Jasmine
Lily (Style Three)
May
Pansy
Petunia
Poppy (Style Two)
Primrose
Rose (Style One)
Veronica (Style Three)
Violet (Style Two)

Famous Shakespeare Roles

Mrs. Patrick Campbell as Juliet

Faye Whittaker's Chilhood Memories Collection

My Pal
Raggetty Anne
Ship Ahoy
Sunday Best (Style Two)

Femmes Fatales

Emma Hamilton
Empress Josephine
Lady Castlemaine
Lillie Langtry
Madame de Pompadour
Marie Antoinette
Mrs. Fitzherbert
Nell Gwynn

Figurine of, The Year

Jacqueline (Style Two), 1995
Karen (Style Two), 1996
Lily (Style One), 1993
Sarah (Style Two), 1994

Flower Ladies

Enchanted Lily
Fairest Lily
Gracious Lily
Sweetest Rose (Style Two)

Flower of Love

Lily (Style Four)

Four Flowers Collection, The

Carnation
Iris (Style Two)
Lily (Style Two)
Rose (Style Two)

Four Seasons

Autumn Leaves
Springtime (Style One)
Summer's Day
Winter Frolic

Gilbert and Sullivan

Jack Point
Judge, The
Mikado
Peep Bo
Pirate Captain
Pitti Sing
Policeman, The
Yum Yum

Golden Age

Alexandra at the Ball
Beatrice at the Garden Party
Charlotte a Royal Debut
Eugenie First Night at the Opera
Georgina Takes Tea with Lady Alice
Grace (Style Two)
Louisa at Ascot

Grosvenor Collection

Anna (Style Two)
Fleur
Lauren (Style One)
Tess

Hampshire Collection, The

Erin

High Society

Lady Sara

High Style Collection

Gina
Jody
Lucinda (Style One)

Historical Figures

Lord Nelson

History of Costume

House of Hanover (1727-1760)
House of Hanover (1790-1837)
House of Hanover, Empire Style (1804-1815)
House of Hanover, George II (1745-1755)
House of Hanover, Victoria (1837-1856)
House of Lancaster (1399-1461)
House of Norman (1066-1154)
House of Plantagenet (1350-1399)
House of Plantagenet, Edward II (1307-1327)
House of Stuart (1603-1714)
House of Stuart (1625-1649)
House of Stuart, James I (1603-1625)
House of Tudor (1485-1603)
House of Tudor (1558-1603)
House of York (1461-1485)
Restoration Stuart (1685-1689)
Restoration Stuart (1660-1689)

Japanese Studies

Boy with Bird
Boy with Butterfly
Girl with Fan
Girl with Mask

Just William

Just William
William the Gangster

Kensington Collection

Chloe (Style One)
Dawn (Style One)
Elisa
Gail (Style One)
Holly (Style One)
Kirsty (Style One)
Laurie Ann
Lesley (Style One)
Selina (Style One)
Sharon (Style One)
Tricia
Zoe (Style One)

King and Country (1940 Period)

Airman (R.A.F 1945)
Landgirl
Sailor, The
Soldier, The

La Belle Epoque

Clementine Debut in Paris
Lady Alice of the Royal Garden Party
Lady Evelyn at the Country House Party
Lady Frances on the Grand Tour
Lady Harriet the Royal Skating Party
Lady Helena Riding in Hyde Park
Lady Rose at the Royal Ascot Ball
Sophie Promenading on the Champs Elysees

Ladies of Fashion

Abigail (Style One)
Adele
Admiration
Affection
After The Ball
Alexis
Alice
Alison (Style One)
Allison
Amanda (Style One)
Amy (Style One)
Angelique
Anna (Style One)
Annabelle (Style One)
Annabelle (Style Two)
Anne (Style One)
Anne Marie
Anthea (Style One)
Anthea (Style Two)
Antonia (Style One)
Antonia (Style Two)
Ashley
Autumn Grace
Ball, The
Barbara Ann
Belinda
Beverley
Bewitching
Birthday Girl, The
Blanche (Style One)
Bolero

Ladies of Fashion (cont.)

Brenda
Bridesmaid (Style Four)
Bridget
Café Royale
Camilla
Candida
Captivation
Carnival
Carol (Style Two)
Caroline (Style One)
Celeste
Charlotte (Style One)
Cheryl
Christabel (Style One)
Christabel (Style Two)
Christina
Christine (Style One)
Clare
Clare Marie
Colleen
Collette
Constance
Crystal
Dance of Dawn
Daphne (Style One)
Davina
Debbie
Demetria
Denise
Devotion
Diana
Diane
Dianne
Donna (Style One)
Dorothy (Style One)
Dorothy (Style Two)
Dorothy (Style Three)
Dulcie
Eileen
Elaine (Style Two)
Elegance
Elizabeth (Style One)
Emily
Emma (Style One)
Emma Jane
Enchanted Evening
Enchantress
Eugenie
Faith
Fay
Felicity
Fiona (Style One)
First Dance
Flair
Flora (Style One)
Flower Girl (Style One)
Frances
Gabrielle
Gail (Style Two)
Gemma (Style One)
Georgina (Style One)
Geraldine
Gillian (Style One)
Gillian (Style Two)
Glenda

Ladies of Fashion (cont.)

Grand Entrance
Greeting, The
Happy Anniversary
Happy Birthday
Harmony
Hayley
Hazel
Heather (Style One)
Heather (Style Two)
Heather (Style Four)
Helen (Style One)
Henrietta
High Society (Style One)
Honeymoon
Honor
Hostess, The
Invitation to the Ball
Isadora
Jan
Jane (Style One)
Janet
Jayne (Style One)
Jean (Style One)
Jean (Style Two)
Jennifer (Style Three)
Joan (Style Two)
Josephine
Joy
Julia (Style One)
Julie (Style One)
Julie (Style Two)
Kate (Style One)
Katherine (Style One)
Kathleen
Kelly
La Belle Creole
Lady in Lace
Laura (Style One)
Leeds Centenary Ball
Leona
Letter From a Lover
Linda (Style One)
Linda (Style Two)
Lindsey
Lisa (Style One)
L'Ombrelle
Lorraine
Louisa
Louise
Love's Dream
Lucy (Style One)
Lynne (Style One)
Madeline
Margaret (Style One)
Maria
Marianne
Marilyn (Style One)
Marjorie
Marlene
Martha
Maureen
Melanie (Style One)
Melissa
Melody
Michele

Ladies of Fashion (cont.)

Miranda
Moira
Monique
"Name Your Own"
Nicole
Norma
Patricia (Style One)
Patricia (Style Two)
Pauline
Peaches and Cream
Peggy
Penelope Ann
Petite
Philippa (Style One)
Polly
Pontefract Princess
Proposal, The
Rachel (Style One)
Rapture
Rebecca (Style One)
Red Rose of Lancashire
Regina
Roberta
Romance (Style One)
Romany Dance
Rosalee
Rosemary (Style One)
Rosemary (Style Two)
Sally Anne (Style One)
Sally Anne (Style Two)
Sarah (Style One)
Serenade (Style One)
Serenity
Shirley
Shona
Silken Lady
Sophia (Style One)
Sophie (Style Two)
Sophisticated Lady (The)
Southern Belle
Special Memories
Special Occasion
Spring Song
Stella (Style One)
Stephanie (Style One)
Stephanie (Style Two)
Strawberry Fayre (Style Two)
Sue
Summer Breeze (Style One)
Summer Days
Summer Romance
Summer Stroll
Sunday Best (Style One)
Susan (Style Two)
Tara
Tenderness, The
Tender Thoughts
Teresa
Thoughts
Tina
Twenty-One Today
Ursula
Valerie
Vanessa (Style One)
Vanessa (Style Two)

Ladies of Fashion (cont.)

Vanity Fayre
Veronica (Style Two)
Vicky
Victoria (Style One)
Victoria (Style Two)
Wakefield Rose
Wendy
White Rose of Yorkshire
Winsome
Winter Stroll
Winter's Morn
Yasmin
Young Love

Ladies of Fashion Figure of the Year

Anne (Style Three)

Ladies of Leisure

After Dark
Belle of the Ball (Style One)
Evening Stroll
Precious Moments

Les Parisiennes

Mademoiselle Cherie

Literary Heroines

Cathy (Style Two)
Rebecca (Style Four)
Scarlett

Little Women

Annette (Style Three)
Claudette (Style One)
Danielle (Style One)
Estelle (Style One)
Giselle (Style One)
Jeanette (Style One)
Juliette (Style One)
Lynette (Style One)
Michelle (Style One)
Nanette (Style One)
Nicolette (Style One)
Paulette (Style One)

London Heritage

Buckingham Palace Guard
Chelsea Pensioner
Grenadier Guard
Tower of London Beefeater
Whitehall Lifeguard

Membership Exclusive

Summertime

Minuettes

Abigail (Style Two)
Chloe (Style Three)
Danielle (Style Three)

Minuettes (cont.)

Emma (Style Three)
Gemma (Style Two)
Grace (Style Three)
Hannah (Style Two)
Holly (Style Three)
Jade
Jessica (Style Two)
Joanne (Style Two)
Kimberley (Style Two)
Leanne
Michelle (Style Three)
Natalie (Style Two)
Rosie (Style Two)
Sophie (Style Three)
Summertime
Zoe (Style Two)

Modern Brides Collection

Vienna

Moments of the Heart

Summer Daydream

National Children's Home

Boy, The
Childhood Joys

Nurses

Crimean Nurse
District Nurse
Great Ormond St. Nurse
Nurse

Old London Streets

Flower Seller, The (Style One)
Match Seller
Muffin Man
Old Lady Feeding Pigeons
Shoe Shine Boy (The)

Park Lane Collection

Belle of the Ball (Style Two)

Queens of England

Mary Tudor (1516-1558)
Queen Anne
Queen Elizabeth I (1533-1603)
Queen Victoria (Style One)

Roaring Twenties (Style One)

Bobbie
Celia
Gilly
Zelda

Roaring Twenties (Style Two)

Blanche (Style Two)
Eve
Kitty (Style Two)
Millie (Style Two)
Phoebe
Sadie

Romance and Legend

Britannia
Dick Turpin

Romance of Henley

Boating Party
Cheering the Crew
First Visit
Winning Stroke

Royal Academy of Dancing, The

Dame Alicia Markova
Dame Antoinette Sibley
Dame Margot Fonteyn

Royal Ascot Miniature Collection

Lady Beatrice
Lady Catherine
Lady Clara
Lady Eliza
Lady Emily
Lady Emma
Lady Evelyn
Lady Florence
Lady Frances
Lady Grace
Lady Helena
Lady Lilian
Lady Louise
Lady Lydia
Lady May
Lady Phoebe
Lady Rose (Style Two)
Lady Sarah

Royal Brides

Princess Alexandra
Queen, The (Style One)
Queen Mary
Queen Mother, The (Style One)
Queen Victoria (Style Two)

Royal Collection

Anne Boleyn
Anne of Cleves
Catherine of Aragon
Catherine Parr
Henry VIII
Jane Seymour
Katherine Howard

Royalty

H.M Queen Elizabeth II (Style Two)
H.M Queen Elizabeth II and H.R.H. Duke of Edinburgh
H.M Queen Elizabeth, The Queen Mother (Style Two)
H.R.H. The Prince of Wales (Style One)
H.R.H. The Prince of Wales (Style Two)
Lady Diana Spencer

R.S.P.C.A

Best Friend

Screen Goddesses

High Society (Style Two)
Moonlight Serenade

Silhouettes

Carole
Eleanor (Style Two)
Gillian (Style Three)
Kay
Lydia (Style Two)
Nicola
Olivia (Style Two)
Philippa (Style Two)
Sally
Suzannah

Somerset Collection

Alexandra (Style One)
Amelia
Arabella
Catherine (Style One)
Charlotte (Style Two)
Elena
Verity
Virginia

Special Events

Alison (Style Two)
Emma (Style Two)
Helen (Style Two)
Margaret (Style Two)
Pamela (Style Two)

Spirits of the Jewels

Emerald
Ruby
Sapphire (Style Two)
Topaz

Sporting Collection, The

Crown, The
First Catch
First Tee
Green, The
Ladies Day
Match Point
Olympic Runner
Shooter, The
Squash Racquets
Winter Slopes

Togetherness

Gift of Love
Helping Hand, A
Mother's Day
Mummy's Little Helper

Turn of The Century

Evening Ball
Henley Royal Regatta
Royal Enclosure at Ascot

Valentine Debutante of the Year

Endless Love
Eternity
My Love, 1994
Sweetheart, 1995

Victorian Elegance

Miss Charlotte
Miss Emily
Miss Jane
Miss Laetita
Miss Sarah

Victorian Seasons

Skater, The

Vogue

Miss 1920
Miss 1921
Miss 1922
Miss 1923
Miss 1924
Miss 1925
Miss 1926
Miss 1927
Miss 1928
Miss 1929

Wedding Collection

Bridesmaid (Style Five)
Follow the Bride
For your Wedding
Groom, The
Pageboy

Wedding Anniversary Collection

My Pearl Wedding Day
My Ruby Wedding Day
My Silver Wedding Day

Welsh Ladies of Fashion

Bethan
Megan
Rhian
Sian

West End Girls

Greta
Marilyn (Style Two)
Sophia (Style Three)
Vivien

When Dreams Come True

An Enchanted Evening

Wimbledon Collection

Tennis Party, The

APPLICATION FORM

Join Coalport Collector

... the society for lovers of beautiful figurines

THE BENEFITS OF MEMBERSHIP

- COALPORT COLLECTOR is a quarterly, full colour magazine with up-to-the-minute news on Coalport figurines, competitions, special offers and features. The magazine includes interviews with collectors and fascinating features from the world of figurines. It gives members the opportunity to exchange news and views and there's also a popular Find and Seek column to help members find, sell and swap figurines with other readers.

- All members joining in 1997 will receive absolutely free a delightful Coalport Minuette figurine called *Summertime.* Worth approximately £30, she is the second of a series of four lovely little figurines being issued exclusively for Coalport collectors.

- An embossed membership card personalised with name and exclusive membership number which allows members free entry to the Wedgewood Museum at Barlaston, Staffordshire, and also to purchase figurines from the exclusive *Collingwood Collection* at their local stockist.

- Members will receive personal invitations to Coalport Collector Events. Organised on a regional basis and in association with major Coalport stockists. Events will include: demonstrations of figurine decoration; talks by craftsmen who will personally sign figurine purchases and previews of new collections.

- Membership certificate personalised with name and exclusive membership number.

- Advance notification of new figurines and when to look out for them in your local stockist.

- Special VIP factory visits organised exclusively for Society members and their guests.

HOW TO JOIN

Simply complete the application form on the reverse of this page, and send it to us together with your cheque or postal order for £20 payable to Coalport Collector for your first years membership. Alternatively you can pay by credit card, Switch or direct debit*. In addition you may wish to enrol a friend or relative as a Coalport Collector. Please see the application form for full details of gift membership.

Applications should be sent to: Laura Collingwood, COALPORT COLLECTOR, P.O. Box 99, Sudbury, Suffolk, England, CO10 6SN

**Direct debit application forms are available at your local stockist or from the address above.*

PERSONAL MEMBERSHIP APPLICATION FORM

Please enrol me as a Coalport Collector for one year at a cost of £20 (UK residents), C$40.00 (Canadian residents), US$40.00 (all others). The Coalport Collector's Society is open to all persons aged 18 or over. Please allow 28 days for delivery of membership pack.

Please complete all details in ink and BLOCK CAPITALS. (Panel A)
Title (*Mr/Mrs/Ms etc*) Sex Male ❑ Female ❑

1st name ____________ 2nd initial ________ Last name ____________

Address ______________________________

Town/City ____________ County ________ Postcode ______ Tel area code _____ No. ________

How would you like your name to appear on your membership card? (*maximum 25 characters including spacing*)

❑❑❑❑❑❑❑❑❑❑❑❑❑❑❑❑❑❑❑❑❑❑❑❑❑

Preferred stockist where you normally purchase your Coalport figurines - and wish to continue.

Stockist's Name ______________________________

Stockist's Address ______________________________

FOR GIFT MEMBERSHIP ONLY

Your friend or relative will be informed in their letter of welcome to the Society that their member ship is a gift from you. Please write in BLOCK CAPITALS your name as you wish it to appear on their letter of welcome.

Please indicate if you wish the gift membership to be sent to your nominated recipient or to you so you can present the gift personally.

Please enrol my friend/relative named below as a COALPORT COLLECTOR. I confirm that he/she is aged 18 or over.
Title (*Mr/Mrs/Ms etc*) Sex Male ❑ Female ❑

1st name ____________ 2nd initial ________ Last name ____________

(Panel B)
ADDRESS OF GIFT MEMBERSHIP RECIPIENT (*must be completed in all cases*)

Address ______________________________

Town/City ____________ County ________ Postcode ______ Tel area code _____ No. ________

How would you like your name to appear on your membership card? (*maximum 25 characters including spacing*)

❑❑❑❑❑❑❑❑❑❑❑❑❑❑❑❑❑❑❑❑❑❑❑❑❑

Tick one:
❑ Please send the membership pack with my compliments direct to my friend or relative at the above address in panel B.
❑ I prefer to present the membership pack to my friend/relative personally; please send it to me at my address in panel A.

METHOD OF PAYMENT

I wish that I and/or my nominated friend/relative be enrolled in the Coalport Collector Society for the period of one year. I understand that membership costs £20/ C$40 / US$40 per person and is open to persons aged 18 or over. I wish to pay by cheque/postal order/credit card/Switch, as shown below. Please make cheques/postal orders payable to COALPORT COLLECTOR.

Signed: ____________________ Date: ____________

Tick One:
❑ I enclose a cheque/postal order for £_____ or $_____ for _____ memberships made payable to Coalport Collector.
(Please ensure your address is written on the back of all cheques)
❑ Please charge my Visa/Access/Mastercard/Switch with the sum of £_____ or $_____ for_____ memberships.

Card No. ❑❑❑❑❑❑❑❑❑❑❑❑❑❑❑❑❑❑❑❑❑❑❑❑❑❑❑❑ Switch Issue No: ❑❑

Expiry date: __________ Name on card: ______________________

Signature: ______________________ Date: ____________

Name and billing address of cardholder (if different from A): Mr/Mrs/Ms ______________________

Address ______________________ Postcode ____________

Please send this form to Laura Collingwood, Coalport Collector, PO Box 99, Sudbury, Suffolk CO10 6SN
Canadian residents please send this form to Waterford Wedgewood Canada, 20 West Beaver Creek Road, Richmond Hill, ON L4B 316